ENERGY: REGIONAL GOALS AND THE NATIONAL INTEREST

A conference sponsored by
the National Energy Project
of the American Enterprise Institute for Public Policy Research

THE AEI
NATIONAL ENERGY PROJECT

The American Enterprise Institute's
National Energy Project was established in early 1974
to examine the broad array of issues
affecting U.S. energy demands and supplies.
The project commissions research into all important
ramifications of the energy problem—economic
and political, domestic and international, private
and public—and presents the results
in studies such as this one.
In addition it sponsors symposia, debates, conferences,
and workshops, some of which are televised.

The project is chaired by Melvin R. Laird,
former congressman, secretary of defense,
and domestic counsellor to the President,
and now senior counsellor of *Reader's Digest*.
The advisory council represents a wide range of
energy-related viewpoints.
Professor Edward J. Mitchell of the University of Michigan
is the project director.

Views expressed are those of the authors
and do not necessarily reflect the views of
either the advisory council and others associated with
the project or of the advisory panels,
staff, officers, and trustees of AEI.

ENERGY: REGIONAL GOALS AND THE NATIONAL INTEREST

Edited by Edward J. Mitchell

American Enterprise Institute for Public Policy Research
Washington, D. C.

ISBN 0-8447-2080-1 (Paper)
ISBN 0-8447-2081-X (Cloth)

Library of Congress Catalog Card No. 76-9611

Printed in the United States of America

MAJOR CONTRIBUTORS

Jim Bishop
Newsweek magazine

David Boren
Governor of Oklahoma

Edward W. Brooke
Senator from Massachusetts

Pete V. Domenici
Senator from New Mexico

Michael J. Dukakis
Governor of Massachusetts

Melvin R. Laird
Chairman, American Enterprise Institute's
National Energy Project

James C. Langdon
Texas Railroad Commission

Charles Murphy
Murphy Oil Corporation

Nelson Rockefeller
Vice President of the United States

Milton Russell
Chief Economist,
Council of Economic Advisers

Jill Schuker
New England Congressional Caucus

Stewart Udall
Overview, Inc.

Frank Zarb
Federal Energy Administration

FOREWORD

In an editorial of June 23, 1975, the editors of the *Washington Post* stated, "Energy policy is now the most divisive regional issue to afflict this country since civil rights." This assertion accorded with my own belief that the energy problem, already a divisive issue pitting the Congress against the administration and the producer against the environmentalist, was causing yet another fissure along regional lines. To address these matters in their political and economic context, on October 2 and 3, 1975, I chaired a conference sponsored by the American Enterprise Institute for Public Policy Research. The conference brought together representatives of the Northeast including Senator Brooke and Governor Dukakis of Massachusetts, representatives of the Southwest including Governor Boren of Oklahoma and Judge Langdon of the Texas Railroad Commission, and representatives of the administration including Vice President Rockefeller, Federal Energy Administrator Zarb, and Chairman Nassikas of the Federal Power Commission. The discussion during those two days helped all of us present to gauge the depth of regional divisions over energy policy, discover some of the causes of these divisions, and work toward some policies of reconciliation. The conference primarily reflected the interest of the participants in oil and natural gas issues, particularly the issue of price. The real problems of regional coal development were unfortunately left unexplored.

New Englanders couch their regional position in terms of equity. They point out that New England consumes per capita more of the high-cost imported oil and less of the low-cost natural gas than any other region of the country. New Englanders pay the highest prices and consume the least energy per capita of the residents of any region in the United States. Senator Brooke pointed out that some New Englanders are paying more for their monthly fuel bill than they do for their mortgage. Further, because of continued higher prices in New England during the 1960s and sharply higher prices during 1973–1975, New England has seen industry move away and unemployment remain far above the national average. Its residents believe themselves unjustly maligned by the charge that New England refuses to help itself in supplying its own needs. They are moving to support drilling off their shores, have attempted to place several refineries in the area, have the highest per capita use of nuclear power in the nation, and are investigating the possibility of coal mining in Massachusetts. Some believe that they are the unjust victims of duplicity on the part of energy producers and the federal government. Throughout the period of the federal mandatory oil import program (1959–1973) they paid—and producers gained through—higher oil prices in the name of national security. Now, they claim, producers are making an about-face and calling for a free market with its concomitant higher price.

If the New England regional energy position is expressed in a desire for equity, the position of Southwest producers is expressed in a desire for trust. Representatives of the Southwest are strongly in favor of oil and gas deregulation. They believe that the energy problem could be solved, at least for the near term, if the producers were given price incentives to explore more difficult new sources and to produce from higher-cost old sources. Producing-state representatives point out that deregulation is an unselfish policy proposal because consumers and industry in Oklahoma, Texas, and Louisiana are the greatest gainers under the policy status quo. The producing states believe that they have been reasonable in their compromise proposals on price deregulation. They are willing to phase in the price rises but see no similar willingness to compromise from the consumers. They sense only an air of distrust which they fear could lead to punitive actions. Judge Langdon pointed to sections of the Stevenson-Hollings bill which make the withholding of oil and gas a crime and said that the producers have "been depicted as criminals and vicious people. As a matter of fact, the way some of the legislation is designed in House bill 9464, some of the repeal provisions are far more severe than those we have to control the Mafia in this country."

Happily, our conference did not end with these perceptions unchanged. First, it became evident that a good deal of the regional bitterness came about because of the suddenness and the size of the changes wrought by the crystalization of the OPEC cartel. The embargo and the price-hikes caused a crisis atmosphere and dislocations that are still being felt through the loss of jobs and incomes. For a time the sudden and direct effects on the pocketbook caused some inflammation and regional language in politics. However, as we move away from the recession of 1974–1975, some elected officials from all regions are beginning to look for a national approach to the long-term problems of energy. Governor Boren pointed out that thirty-one governors, including those from producing and consuming states, were able to agree recently on a national energy program. The program which they approved was the result not only of each governor's perception of his own state's local interests, but also of the willingness to give and take that is the hallmark of politics at its best. The question which both Governor Boren and Senator Domenici put to the conference was, When will the Congress settle down to the same process and evolve an energy program for the nation?

Both the reason why this question must be posed and the answer to the question were at first startling to me. The conference participants—particularly Gwen Murphree, president of the League of Women Voters, and Stewart Udall, former secretary of the interior—found that the public has had no widespread or deep understanding of energy policy problems. Before any program can become politically acceptable, the people must be disabused of the notion that the energy situation is contrived or ephemeral. Stewart Udall likened the views of some to the desire for exorcism of an oil industry devil-spirit. The consensus of the conference called for political leadership on this matter. This bipartisan gathering of national and regional energy experts was much less divided on the nature of the problem and its solution than is the current leadership in Congress. This is significant, for it means that if the perceptions of the experts can be transmitted to the legislators, and if they in turn will stand on this knowledge before their constituents, this nation can stop its passive drift toward the dangers of another embargo.

Once the people, through their legislators, have come to accept the reality of an energy problem, they can begin to come to agreement on such substantive issues as energy pricing. Experts of all persuasions agreed that the big gainers under natural gas price controls were consumers in the oil- and gas-producing states who can get most of the gas they need at the low interstate prices and all the rest they desire at the higher intrastate prices. For some New England consumers the price of new gas is in effect infinite since they cannot get gas at any price. The response of all concerned was to urge a higher price to equalize the price of gas with oil and to bring out further supplies. The response of supply to price was pointed out repeatedly by Chairman Nassikas. The need for negotiation, political give and take, was narrowed to the question whether all gas should be priced at \$1.30/Mcf or whether the average should remain far under \$1.30/Mcf but new contracts should be allowed to go to the neighborhood of \$2.00/Mcf. A consensus likewise emerged in the discussion on oil. Conference participants agreed that the price of oil should not be held artificially low through government regulations. Here the experts agreed for different reasons. Elvis Stahr, president of the Audubon Society, and Stewart Udall believed that the policy would bring about conservation of precious resources, while Charles DiBona of the American Petroleum Institute and Governor Boren emphasized that the policy would work for more oil. Jill Schuker of the New England Congressional Caucus and Senator Brooke questioned whether the average price of U.S. oil should be allowed to approach the OPEC monopoly price of \$13.50/barrel. As with natural gas, however, the differences between the points of view were narrow and within a range in which negotiation can take place. There were no fundamental or irreconcilable regional issues.

One lesson I learned from the conference participants is that there can be no unique regional approaches to this national energy problem. Regional disparities in resource endowments are the rule, not the exception, in this transcontinental nation. However, our economic strength comes from the ability of each region to specialize in the production of those commodities for which it is best suited and to buy from other regions those commodities which would be higher-cost if produced at home. Through this system we are all made richer and the lowest costs emerge over all. Government intervention—whether an oil import quota or natural gas price controls—interrupts this process. The government hopes to award its favors impartially but often (as in the case of energy) the intervention benefits one region at the expense of another. A second lesson of the conference was to reinforce a new perception that has become increasingly clearer since I took on the chairmanship of the National Energy Project at AEI over one year ago. The energy problem is now largely one of political statesmanship. The facts are known within reasonable bounds. Our national political leaders must measure up in responsibility to the authority which is theirs.

MELVIN R. LAIRD

CONTENTS

PART FOUR
Energy Policy: A New War Between the States?

David Boren
Edward Brooke
Stewart Udall
Frank Zarb
Melvin R. Laird, Moderator

PART ONE

The Economics of Regional Interests
in Energy

INTRODUCTION

Michael Dukakis

Nearly two years have passed since the Arab oil embargo of 1973, and we are still without a working national energy program. Despite all the attention that has been given this issue by the states, and the Congress, and the President—or perhaps because of all this attention—we have not been able to reach agreement on a national energy policy.

The individual states are clearly not united, but I am convinced the reason for their lack of unity has more to do with the ways of nature than of politics. The fact is that only a few states in this country are blessed with an abundant natural supply of energy resources. Some 65 percent of this country's oil and gas is produced in just three states. Most of our uranium is found in two states, and most of our coal is taken from five. All told, fully 60 percent of America's energy supplies can be found in just seven states. Ironically, the possession of vast energy resources has not produced unqualified benefits for those states. For a while, they have reaped considerable profits, but they have also suffered environmental damage and have often felt the effects of the boom-and-bust syndrome.

We in the consuming states recognize our debt to the producing states. Our industries and our utilities have long burned coal from the fields of West Virginia and Pennsylvania. We heat our homes with oil and natural gas from Texas and Louisiana, and many of our power companies use uranium from the Rocky Mountain states. I might add that we have certainly paid our dues. New England residents and businesses pay higher energy prices than anyone else in the country, and those higher prices have traditionally been our lot. As a result, we have been forced to learn to live with less, to conserve in our homes, our cars, our businesses, and—I might add—in state government as well. In fact, in Massachusetts during these past several months, we have developed for the first time in state government a strict plan for conserving energy in every one of our state-run buildings, and we expect (or are shooting for a goal of) some 20 percent reduction in the use of energy in state government alone. Figures recently published by the Commerce Department show that New England industry has conserved energy at a rate three times better than the national average. In fact, we in New England and the Northeast are using far less energy per capita than is used in any other region in the country.

New England's lack of indigenous energy sources has also forced us to rely heavily on foreign suppliers of fuel, which is one reason why my administration, along with the administrations in other New England states, is serious about wanting careful and well-planned exploration of offshore oil resources. Even so, until we know more about those resources—and we are currently reviewing and studying them, dealing both with the potential energy sources offshore and with their impact on our coastline, on our environment, and on our economy—we are still faced with an over-reliance on imported energy.

I do not hear much disagreement these days about the need for proper development of our strategic oil reserves, and I do not hear any argument about the need to take further steps to conserve energy. The disagreement, it seems, arises when we deal with specific issues like energy pricing, tariffs on imported fuels, and the rate of energy growth. I hope that during this conference we will have a chance to discuss the costs and benefits of energy particular to each region of the country. Everyone, whether from Massachusetts or Texas or Oklahoma or Alaska, has felt the impact of the energy crisis. And if we have learned one thing since the 1973 embargo, it is that we are all in this together. I hope our discussions today will prove to be a step toward a better understanding of our collective problems and toward a national energy policy.

Our first panelist is Milton Russell, a senior staff economist for the Council of Economic Advisers. He is on leave from Southern Illinois University, where he is a professor of economics. His special areas of interest are energy economics and the economics of regulated industry.

Our second panelist is Charles Murphy, chairman and chief executive officer of Murphy Oil Corporation. From 1939 until the corporation was chartered in 1950, he was an independent oil producer. He serves on the National Petroleum Council and on the Executive and Management Committees of the American Petroleum Institute, where he is currently the chairman of the Conservation Liaison Committee, a group of oil company chief executives who have undertaken to understand the point of view of the conservation organizations of this country and to transmit to the conservationists the point of view of the oil industry.

Third, we have Jill Schuker, who spent some time in the State House in Boston before moving on to greater things in Washington. She is the executive director of the New England Congressional Caucus, which serves as a focal point and liaison for New England's legislative and economic concerns. Formerly she served as a special assistant to Congressman Michael Harrington in areas dealing with energy and as legislative assistant to the president of the Massachusetts state senate. A graduate of Skidmore College and the Tufts University Graduate School, she holds a master's degree in political science.

THE IMPACT OF ALTERNATIVE REGULATION POLICIES

Milton Russell

I shall concentrate this morning on regional interests in energy consumption. Because of the time limit on this presentation, I have chosen to ignore the producing side entirely, despite the important regional ramifications of energy production or, for example, environmental quality and income distribution. I wish to explore, instead, the impact on consumers, by region, of alternative policies toward the regulation of the price of oil and of the field price of natural gas. Before I proceed, however, it would perhaps be worthwhile to identify two other consumption-related regional issues, or supposedly regional issues.

First, let us consider the concern of the nonproducing regions that have been made worse off by the relative increase in energy prices. On reflection, I think we can see this is not really a regional issue, though some have treated it as if it were. This is a consumer issue, and consumers of energy exist in all portions of the nation. Each of them in his current role as a consumer would prefer lower energy prices to higher. The issue, though, is whether, in his broader role as citizen (and as future consumer), he would be made better off or worse off by oil and gas decontrol and the higher prices that would follow. The penalty of higher current prices must be balanced against greater national economic output from a more efficient use of resources, against a higher rate of domestic production of all energy, against a lower level of energy consumption and consequent environmental degradation, against a lower level of oil imports and, ultimately, against a lower level of risk from some possible future politically motivated oil embargo. Clearly, this is an important question on which strong opinions are held, but it is not really a regional issue. Perhaps the quality of public discussion would be improved if we would stop treating it as if it were.

The second effect of generally higher energy prices has been to increase the relative costs of living and working in regions where energy is used more intensively than it is elsewhere. Decontrol, we must recognize, would make these disparities in costs greater. Heating oil may be no more expensive per gallon in New England than it is in the South, but a doubling of its cost produces a greater budget impact in a cold climate than in a warm one. Gasoline may not be more expensive in Los Angeles than in New York City, or in New Mexico than in Rhode Island, but differences in lifestyle, population density, and availability of alternative transportation make its cost more important to some consumers than

5

to others. We must recognize that higher energy prices will bring marginal population and production shifts out of areas which by their innate characteristics induce an energy-intensive consumption pattern.

This change, like all changes, is disruptive and disturbing, especially to those adversely affected. But it is no different in kind from many other changes going on about us all the time. We must recognize that to attempt to hold back the regional and other adjustments that follow from energy price-hikes imposed by OPEC is to leave the economy less productive than it would otherwise be and less able to meet the future shocks that inevitably will follow in our dynamic world.

With that point out of the way, I would like now to turn to my major topic, the effect of alternative regulatory policies on the regional availability and price of oil and natural gas. We can consider oil first.

None of the three likely policies—continued controls, phased decontrol, or instant decontrol of oil prices—is likely to affect the regional availability of oil. So long as oil can be freely imported, there will be no shortages, and we can therefore ignore the availability question. The price question is a little more complex, but the answer is similar. Regional differences in the price of petroleum products are not likely to be much affected by which of these policies is chosen, though of course the level of prices will be.

The price of petroleum products coming out of a refinery in the current regulated environment is a function almost exclusively of the cost of crude oil going in; and that cost is largely equalized by the so-called entitlements program, which gives each refinery the equivalent of the same proportion of low-cost controlled crude oil. The entitlements program does not of course make up for other cost differentials that remain—these being mainly transportation costs. Consumers in regions remote from refineries, refineries in regions remote from producing or importing centers, and producers remote from refineries who can use their product suffer the disadvantages of location, just as those who are not remote gain its advantages.

This same disadvantage or advantage (and no other) would exist under phased decontrol or immediate decontrol policies, again ignoring minor adjustments. During the period when phased decontrol was taking place, the interregional differentials would remain unchanged because the entitlements program would remain in force just as it remains in force during a period of continued controls. On the other hand, in the case of immediate decontrol, all oil of the same quality— whether previously controlled, uncontrolled, or imported—would move toward the same price, again ignoring transportation cost. Consequently—and I think this is an important conclusion—the interregional differences in refined product prices would reflect location alone.

Now, the general conclusion that there is little regional impact on oil price and availability from alternative energy policies must take into account special factors affecting residual fuel oil and propane. Both residual oil and propane are regionally important; residual oil in those coastal regions, and propane in the Midwest and South. The prices paid for residual oil under the current control program already reflect world crude prices. Therefore these prices will not change with either immediate or phased decontrol, or with a continuation of the current control program. Consequently, as decontrol occurs, the average price of petroleum products consumed will rise less in regions with more than proportionate consumption of residual oil than it will rise in other regions.

The propane market offers special problems because propane, while it has special uses of its own, is also a prime substitute for natural gas. Propane's long-term supply and demand are elastic—supply because propane can be imported, and demand because users of propane for bulk heat can switch to other fuels. In the short term, however, some possibility exists that a surge in demand for propane as a substitute for natural gas might drive its price upward so rapidly as to bring serious difficulties to its historical consumers in the Midwest and the South. The President has requested temporary authority to control the price and direct the allocation of propane if the current general controls on the petroleum industry expire. The regional interests in propane supply and price, both of which would no doubt be substantially altered by a change in control policy, would be accommodated by a limited extension of control if the President's requests were honored.

We can then summarize the regional impact of different oil policies by saying that a policy that leads to higher prices for fuel could temporarily exacerbate the problems inherent in some regions' being more fuel-intensive than others. It could also lead to earlier adjustments by consumers and producers to higher energy prices than would maintaining the current program. On a direct regional comparison, however, which is the topic of our discussion today, none of these policies would substantially alter the interregional differentials in petroleum prices or availability.

The situation for natural gas differs from the situation for oil because the current control process affects gas availability as well as gas price. Price controls on natural gas mean that there is not enough natural gas to go around, so that here we face the availability question foursquare. We are probably all familiar with the fact that in the producing states, consumers actually have the best of both worlds under current regulation of natural gas. Producing-state consumers are assured of supplies because they can bid high enough in the unregulated intrastate market to obtain gas, but the price they must pay is lower than it would be if interstate consumers were also allowed to bid for gas. Consequently, consumers in producing regions are now obtaining gas at prices below what they would have to pay for alternative fuels, and they have the advantages of the superior burning characteristics of gas as well.

In the interstate regulated markets, the condition is different. Some interstate consumers—and I must say that if the estimates of this winter's curtailments are borne out, this is going to be a rapidly declining number—are able to obtain gas priced according to the low, regulated, controlled field price. Other consumers though, including both those whose supplies have been cut off and those who were never allowed to connect to the gas system in the first place, face what amounts to an infinitely high price for gas. They cannot get gas at all. These latter consumers are forced to switch to other fuels at effective prices substantially higher than the price for gas, or else do without. And doing without is an intensely regional issue. The way some industries do without gas is to close or to move to a producing region where gas availability is assured.

Unlike government policy in the case of oil, then, government policy has created regional disparities in natural gas availability and price. The current policy has brought lower energy costs in the producing area and higher energy costs in the nonproducing areas, and has motivated industry to relocate in the Southwest. In contrast, as Governor Dukakis said earlier, it is climatic and locational conditions that have affected the regional differentials in expenditures for oil.

Decontrol of new gas contracts in the field would lessen this regional discrimination by eliciting more gas supply and by reducing consumption by those to whom gas is worth less than it is to others. Gas decontrol would ultimately eliminate the regional disparity in gas availability, with all the disruption and interregional location changes that it has created. It would tend to equalize the price consumers in different regions pay for fuel—again, ignoring transportation cost. The price result would be that in each region some consumers would find their fuel costs (not their gas costs) higher, and others would find their fuel costs lower. The nation as a whole, of course, would use its limited gas supply more efficiently, would locate industry more efficiently, would increase the production of domestic energy, and would import less insecure energy from abroad.

In summary, then, in the oil policy alternatives that appear to lie before us, there is not much of a purely regional interest. Oil will be available whatever price control policy is adopted, and the differentials in its price among regions will be roughly the same as they are now. There are some regional interests in gas policy. These differences exist not because one region is a producing region and another is not, contrary to some views, but because under existing regulation, consumers in some states are able to buy all the gas they want, while those in others cannot.

REGIONALISM AND THE PUBLIC INTEREST IN ENERGY

Charles Murphy

Mr. Russell, Ms. Schuker and I have each been asked to present in ten-minute statements our views concerning regional interests and the national interest in energy. I could return nine minutes and fifty seconds of my allotted time to our distinguished moderator, because my view is best expressed in one sentence: in this nation there is no regional interest.

The framers of our Constitution saw to that when they said in Article I, Section 10, "No State shall, without the Consent of the Congress, lay any Impost or Duties on Imports or Exports, except what may be absolutely necessary for executing it's inspection Laws." And they provided in Article I, Section 8, that only Congress can regulate commerce, and moreover, that "all Duties, Imposts and Excises shall be uniform throughout the United States." Now, we are not here to celebrate the Republic's Bicentennial, much less the 200th anniversary of *The Wealth of Nations*. But let us reflect on these fundamentals for just a moment.

A nation was being born—not an Attic League, not a Hanseatic League, not a coprosperity sphere, nor any other kind of loose regional grouping, brought together in ad hoc response to military threat on one hand or to exploit mercantile opportunity on the other, but a unified political and economic organism—whose life expectancy transcended given threats or opportunities, however foreboding or beckoning those might have seemed at the moment. We mortals are fallible. We are susceptible, in or out of office, to the virus of overreaction to real or perceived local or temporary emergencies. But so far as the body politic has enjoyed immunity because of the inoculations drawn, so to say, from vials 8 and 10 of the medicine chest. The effect of these inoculations is long lasting. Moreover, they were bolstered by a powerful series of booster shots against sectionalism administered over the period 1861 to 1865. Governor Dukakis, your side beat the hell out of us!

What are the fruits of this to society insofar as industry and commerce are concerned? They include the economies of regional specialization, advantages of scale in transportation, optimization of size and site for manufactures. And it seems no coincidence to me, after 200 years of development unstunted by regionalism, that on the world scene the only rival worthy of our steel is the Soviet Union—a diametrically opposed political system to be sure, but having this in common with us: industry and commerce organized according to a continental rationale.

Should you infer from this introduction that I wish for all mankind similar but even greater advantages on a world scale, you would be right. And were I an idealist, my eyes would dance with visions of opulence for the race. But I am not. A realist understands that in this life, and for all I know the next, sovereigns invoking the national interest are prone to frustrate the impartial market's allocation of resources. They hoard their own, even at the risk of obsolescence, before time of internal need or the hoped-for sale at a higher price. They fend off lower-cost raw materials from abroad, saddling their people with high-cost indigenous sources. They attempt to claim benefits of value added by manufacture, even at unconscionable cost. So be it. Let us sketch some examples how this works in energy, our subject for these two days, and then view our national policies against that background sketch.

For the sake of simplicity—but, granted, perhaps too simplistically—I waive the embargo as an aberration. The leading OPEC nations, Saudi Arabia and Iran, intend to force construction of as much as 3 million barrels a day refining capacity in their countries. They may get about a third of it done. Their motives are understandable, even commendable: industrialization of backward regions, enlargement of an elite professional corps, job opportunities for the semiskilled. But so far as the world community is concerned at present, no new capacity is needed. Scarce capital, whether expressed as tons of goods or in some nation's currency, will be expended to duplicate plants already in place.

A great deal of oil has been found in the North Sea. It is needed, at least so far as the West is concerned, to shorten hauls and for geographical diversification of supply. But the Norwegians are saying, "After all, we are only a small country. We are not so sure we want to face the impact of development once our own requirements are in sight. So maybe we will wait a while." This, too, is understandable from their parochial point of view, but it amounts to denial of a clear need of their neighbors.

Britain will have oil and gas equal to her internal needs with (say) a million barrels a day beyond that. Her oil will be low in sulphur content, high in gasoline yield, precisely suited to the market pattern and processing schemes of North America. The world community's interest would be served by moving British oil in existing tankers from the Shetlands to North American ports via the Great Circle Route, whilst continuing to supply Thames estuary refineries with high-fuel-oil-yielding Middle Eastern crudes. But this is not to be, certainly not in full measure. The United Kingdom is sure to insist that British oil be refined in British refineries for British use and that the exportable surplus, to the maximum extent possible, be in the form of finished products. This is understandable when seen through U.K. spectacles, but, again, costly to the world at large.

One cannot be quite so charitable when turning to Canada. What the Canadians are doing is downright silly, whether seen from inside or out. They are sacrificing on the altar of national self-sufficiency a hard-won market in the

U.S. northern tier, when it is clear they will need that market for their heavy oils (which must be developed on a large scale or not at all). Moreover, their provinces, unlike our states, do have the power to regulate commerce.

Alberta is saying that it soon may prohibit export to British Columbia. Alberta is saying to Ontario, almost in these words, "Vengeance is ours for the long decades the agrarian West has suffered at the hands of the effete industrial East." Ontario retaliates with a refined product price freeze which, if not lifted, will force the shutdown of refineries just at onset of the heating season. It is hardly an exaggeration to say that all this is putting strains on confederation. We could go on *ad nauseam,* but let us stop with Canada, so as to contrast that sordid state of affairs with the state of affairs in our own happy land.

Now, we do some particularly stupid things at our borders and internally at the national decision level. Consider, for example, the cocoon of crude oil import quotas to protect the independent producer. The protection did him no good. Its principal effects were to force the export of refining expansion and to set the stage for OPEC's bold move in late 1973. Another example is freezing the price of natural gas at its by-product level to "protect" the consumer, who now cannot get natural gas at any price. But the safeguards of the Constitution save us from our own folly internally and at the political subdivision levels.

Shortly after the first large-diameter gas lines were built from Louisiana to the East and all the way to New England, there was a coal strike. The Louisiana legislature, in special session as I remember, solemnly enacted an embargo on gas. The federal courts struck that embargo down summarily. Later, Texas producers began to talk of the "unfairness" of Louisiana crude's being "imported" into the Beaumont refining complex. Ridicule was sufficient to dispose of that talk.

It has been this absolute and unconditional interdiction of the parochial interest that has secured to the nation at large the immense benefits of a continental infrastructure. Now it seems the locals are going to have another try at promoting parochial interests. The railroads want to deny the right of eminent domain to coal slurry pipelines so they can head them off at the rail right-of-way. Western interests, in the guise of protecting the environment (which must be done, can be done, and will be done, in any case), would deny coal and shale oil to the Midwest and to New England, when one suspects that the real motive is to hoard water for some real or imaginary need of the twenty-first century.

I hope that my successor on this program will tell us something different. But now it seems to me that New England is searching for some way to become the Ontario of the United States. Let me make it clear what I mean. The price of crude has been raised by Alberta: Alberta itself sets the price, although the federal government in Ottawa has agreed to it. But, in an attempt to cause both the federal government and Alberta to roll back the price, Ontario has put in a freeze. At the federal level, there had been a price freeze geared to exhaustion of some low-cost inventories: they were exhausted, and the freeze was lifted—or, actually, the prices are still controlled, but an increase was allowed. Then Ontario, which does have the power to do this under their system, put in a provincial freeze. This was simply a power play on Ontario's part to force its sister province to back down. And I am afraid that our human tendency to overreact would similarly cause our neighbors in New England to do exactly what Ontario did, had they the power to do so under our political system. I hope Ms. Schuker will tell me that there is nothing whatever to this fear.

Are we to have global rationalization, nationalism, or sectionalism? "No" to the first, sadly, because it is an impossible dream. To enlightened nationalism "yes," because it is the next best thing. To sectionalism "no," because there is no place for it in this nation. It must be shouted down.

THE ENERGY CONCERNS OF NEW ENGLAND

Jill Schuker

Mr. Murphy has raised an interesting point that there may not really be regional interests in energy. Mr. Russell, in a different context, also touched on this, saying that high energy cost is a consumer problem rather than a regional problem. We in New England, however, are faced with inequitable situations, and although we certainly are not the only affected area, equity is an issue and is especially an issue for New England. Today, on behalf of the twenty-five New England Congressional Caucus House members, I would like to focus on the energy concerns of New England.

The New England states and the energy-producing regions of the United States have differed over energy policy during much of the postwar era. New England is the major oil-dependent region of the country—85 percent dependent compared to 45 percent oil dependency in the nation, and 70 percent dependency on natural gas in the oil-producing states. New England, as everyone knows, was during the 1960s and early 1970s and is now a high-cost energy area. Less widely understood is the fact that its energy-cost position has deteriorated seriously recently in comparison with the energy-cost position of other regions.

Despite the fact that industrial energy costs in New England actually fell about 10 percent during the 1960s, industrial energy costs there were about 50 percent above the national average. The cost of the fuel we use—oil—has gone up much more than the costs of the natural gas and coal that are used more in other areas. During the 1960s and 1970s, the West-South-Central and Mountain producing states enjoyed by far the lowest energy costs in the nation. While these states always argue for higher energy prices, it is by and large their consumers and their industries that have benefited most from low prices. Rapid industrial and population growth in these regions certainly has been closely linked to low energy costs. Higher energy prices will help their fuel-producing industries, but they will hurt the industrial interests in these states that have profited enormously from past U.S. energy policies.

One cornerstone energy policy during the 1960s was the Mandatory Oil Import Program in effect from 1959 to 1973. That program has lain at the root of New England's disproportionately high energy prices. The Mandatory Oil Import Program kept the U.S. oil price above world "free market levels" and, despite the fact that quotas came off residual oil in 1966, the continuation of quotas on crude

13

and heating oil kept New England behind the eight-ball. Even after the President's Import Quota Task Force recommended removal of the quota in 1969, we waited another three years until the recommendation was carried out.

During the time it was in effect, New England congressional leaders focused on the oil import program as a key to the energy policy dilemma for New England. And this was done for sound economic reasons. In 1970, the President's task force, headed by George Shultz, suggested that the cost to the nation's consumers from higher oil prices as a result of the import program was $4.8 billion per year, about $400 million of which fell on New England. On a per capita basis, New England bore much more than a fair share of the burden.

During this time as well, in 1968 and 1969, New England strongly supported development of the Machiasport (Maine) refinery. New Englanders are often accused of turning their backs on refinery development, but indeed, it was those from the producing states—including Mr. Wynne from Murphy Oil, Judge Langdon, and Colorado Governor and future Energy Chief John Love—who traveled to Maine to testify against the proposed refinery. Once the Machiasport decision slipped into the 1960s and the Shultz task force report was rejected, the momentum and the leverage to get the refinery were gone.

The most recent and farthest-along refinery effort in New England, the Gibbs proposal in Sanford, Maine, has now run into serious trouble because Burmah Oil, one of the major partners, has gone bankrupt. Until the problem with Burmah, this proposal was running a strong course in New England with state, local, and federally elected public officials—and the Environmental Protection Agency— strongly behind it.

New Englanders have adapted to higher energy prices by reducing energy consumption. The six New England states in 1972 were 21st, 38th, 43rd, 44th, 47th, and 49th in per capita energy consumption. By contrast, Wyoming ranks number 1, Louisiana number 2, Texas number 4—all of these of course being producing states. Per capita energy use was probably three times as high in producing areas as in New England. Energy conservation in New England has been even more marked since the 1973 embargo than it was before. In New England residual oil consumption dropped 18 percent from 1973 to 1974 as prices rose, but only 4.9 percent in the rest of the nation. Similarly, heating oil consumption dropped 8.4 percent in New England, but only 4.6 percent in the rest of the nation.

As a result of the dramatic increase in oil prices in 1974, the cost of energy as a percent of the value of manufacturing shipments in New England jumped about 30 percent above the national average, despite the fact that our industries are conserving fuel and our manufacturing mix is heavily weighted toward low-energy production. At least partly as the result of this deterioration of our energy cost situation, regional unemployment has risen by about 300,000 workers in the past year. In 1974, the unemployment rate in New England averaged 18 percent above the national average. In June 1975, it stood at 11.5 percent—34 percent above the national average.

Moreover, because of New England's climate—and Mr. Russell touched on this point—consumers in the region use 30 percent more fuel and electricity for home temperature control than do consumers in other areas. This means that in addition to the employment impact of higher energy prices, the higher fuel oil prices also have a large dollar impact on the buying power of consumers in the region. It is true that consumers in the rest of the nation use more gasoline than do consumers in New England, but this only partially reduces this impact imbalance, because gasoline prices have gone up much less than heating oil prices over the past year.

This is the outline of the problem. The question is what can be done about it? The answer appears to be that the region should do everything in its power to reduce energy cost differentials. It is energy cost differentials among oil, gas, and coal, not the absolute cost of energy, that are hurting us badly in New England. Oil price equalization is helpful, but it is not a full solution to our problems. We need a reduction in the energy price differential among natural gas, coal, and oil.

Equalization can be achieved in various ways. Obviously the way most New Englanders and most consumers elsewhere in the nation would prefer to achieve it would be to lower the price of oil. Of course, even the most recent oil pricing bill—passed by the House on 23 September 1975—would only roll back some domestic oil prices to $8.50 a barrel, leaving oil-reliant New England dependent on an energy source at least three times as expensive as gas. Another approach, much more inflationary and unlikely, would be to let the price of natural gas rise to a level equivalent to the world price of oil, about $13.50 a barrel. A compromise third "reregulation" approach might be to lower oil prices somewhat—Senators Stevenson, Hollings, Javits, and Brooke have suggested $9.00 a barrel—but to raise natural gas prices to comparable levels.

At the present time, New England, far from benefiting from Federal Power Commission price controls on natural gas, is the region where consumers benefit the least. At a time when the national average price of natural gas is 68.9 cents per million Btus, less than one-third the price of oil, New England per capita consumption of natural gas is about 22.3 percent of the national average, and only 7.2 percent of per capita consumption in the West-South-Central producing region. If natural gas prices were to be raised, the gainers would be the producers, naturally in the producing states, but most of the burden of increased costs would fall at the first stage on industries and consumers also in the producing states, and in the states nearby who at present are the principal beneficiaries of FPC-controlled natural gas prices. Distant New England consumers of industrial products produced in these areas would eventually bear part of the burden, but New England would gain relative to other areas.

15

This, of course, is a political hot potato. The New England Congressional Caucus would have to consider adding yet another cost hike to consumer gas bills. And other approaches could help to lower New England energy costs. Nuclear plants were designed some years ago to compete with residual oil at $2.10 per barrel. It is to be hoped that despite huge cost increases, safe nuclear plants can still produce electricity at lower prices than fossil-fuel plants. Nuclear plants are being considered in New England. The region already uses more nuclear energy— about 20 percent of its total electric output is from nuclear sources—than any other region, and more plants will very possibly be built.

A regional shift back to coal as a utility fuel is also a possibility. New England shifted from coal to oil after World War II because major U.S. oil companies offered residual oil on long-term contract at prices that made coal unattractive. By 1960, long before the advent of the environmentalists, almost no coal was being burned in New England. Since the time when the region shifted from coal to oil for economic reasons, major impediments of a noneconomic character have developed to the renewed burning of coal.

Environmental concerns are real, of course, but even if environmental problems were solved by scrubbers or similar technology, transportation facilities needed to bring coal to the region are lacking, and new mine development would be costly. The New England Congressional Caucus is a strong supporter of federal legislation to rebuild the bankrupt Northeast railroads from Illinois to the Atlantic. No mass conversion back to coal can take place until transportation facilities are adequately repaired. It is to be hoped that producing-state legislators, recognizing that rebuilding the nation's railroads can make increased coal use economically more practical, will join New England in pressing for an important rebuilding and revitalization program. It is also to be hoped that they will focus on the need to develop Eastern deepmined coal if New England is to reduce her dependence on foreign oil.

A Project Independence analysis suggests that coal may be brought to New England in unit trains from Eastern deepmine areas for about $10.00 per ton, but that it would cost $21.00 or $22.00 to bring coal from Montana or New Mexico in the same manner. The difference is the equivalent of $2.00 a barrel or more. No one should expect New England to be greatly tempted to give up high-cost oil for high-cost coal. Coal conversion cannot be separated from the cost of coal and particularly from the cost of coal transportation.

There is some possibility that there are coal fields in southeastern Massachusetts, and federal-state matching funds are being sought to finance the tests necessary to judge the full extent of these fields. Governor Dukakis and the Massachusetts congressional delegation have written to the Bureau of Mines and the National Science Foundation, asking for matching funds to do such tests.

Outer continental shelf development is also important for New England. But just as they are concerned about the environmental impact of additional nuclear capacity and coal conversion, New Englanders are concerned about the onshore and offshore environmental impact of outer continental shelf development. This concern is not at all unreasonable, inasmuch as fishing and tourism are two of the most important New England industries. I think there is an understandably cautious New England attitude toward outer continental shelf development with a real appreciation for the role of the states in outer continental shelf decisions, but there is basic agreement in New England about moving ahead with exploration on the Georges Bank.

The congressional delegation is also strongly in favor of a major storage program that would be an important step on the road to energy independence. The Jackson bill in the Senate has a strong storage program provision as does the recently passed House Bill 7014. As we see it, storage ought to be a cornerstone of any Project Independence for energy.

In summary, the New England region has special needs and problems. We are at present far from gas sources and oil sources. We have high transportation costs. High regional energy costs raise other costs of doing business. The degree to which this is the case is unclear but there is a "ripple effect" from these energy costs that ought to be better examined and understood by regional economists. The New England Congressional Caucus made this point in a meeting with Council of Economics Advisor Burton Malkiel and he agreed with this "ripple effect" thesis. An energy meeting is taking place in Martha's Vineyard, organized by the Boston Federal Reserve Bank and focusing on the New England region's energy picture. A paper for this meeting by the bank's chief economists, Robert Eisenmenger and Richard Syron, makes the point that the region's competitive position is determined not by the absolute price of oil, but by the price of oil relative to other fuels. I think this is the crucial point—one that needs further exploration and that, while it is understood in discussions of inflation, is often less understood in energy terms. Results of this meeting and of the Reserve Bank meeting should stimulate the needed dialogue on this point and others. As Dr. Mitchell points out in his *U.S. Energy Policy: A Primer*, the present energy shortage is essentially a public policy question.

DISCUSSION

JUDGE LANGDON: I would like to add one thing to the remarks by Ms. Schuker. The state of Texas did oppose the Machiasport operation, not on the grounds that it was a refinery, but because we opposed granting to Occidental the import exception that would have permitted it to move 350,000 barrels of crude oil per day under the import quotas. At that time those quotas were worth about a dollar-and-a-half to a dollar. So there was a minimum $350,000-a-day bonus to whoever built that refinery. We were opposing that bonus, not the construction of the refinery.

The second thing I would like to comment on is the figures that Ms. Schuker was using on the per capita consumption of the various states. I am glad to learn that the state of Massachusetts has a possibility of developing coal somewhere. Right now, that state is almost a basket case, as far as producing any of its own energy is concerned. But the state of Wyoming, if its individual citizens used absolutely no energy for their own personal use, would still rank very high in per capita consumption, simply because Wyoming is a state with a small population and large industries—industries providing coal and oil and gas for New Englanders. Again, this is a regional thing. And I think we will have to stop our anti-regional rhetoric if we are going to accomplish anything.

We in Texas are tired of being attacked on the question how much energy we use on a per capita basis. It has been remarked that we rank fourth, and we do: we rank below the state of Louisiana. But both Texas and Louisiana consume a tremendous amount of energy in the production of energy. About 25 percent of the total refining capacity in the United States is located in Texas. It takes the equivalent of about 350,000 barrels per day of crude oil just to operate those refineries. That use is charged against our per capita consumption. We also produce a lot of synthetic fibers and materials for plants in Massachusetts as well, through our petrochemical plants. That production also takes energy, and the situation is not one of an avaricious Texan who is using a lot more energy than his neighbor in New England, just because he wants to use more energy.

But I am delighted to learn that New England is looking toward the development of the Georges Bank of the continental shelf.

MS. SCHUKER: On that, just a couple of points. One is that I have read the comments made by Judge Langdon and by Governor Love and others in relation to Machiasport. Unfortunately, whatever the reasons, the result was the same—the refinery did not come into existence. And I think that is the point. It is often said that the New Englanders have not supported refinery development. As a matter of fact, when the congressional delegation had Governor Love in, when he became the first head of the Federal Energy Office here in Washington, that was one of the changes he threw at us. Of course, given the circumstances, we threw it back. An additional point is that, as has been said already, we are looking into energy development in New England.

One of the arguments we have not made—despite what Judge Langdon says—is that the southern states in general, and Texas in particular, are using a great deal of energy themselves. This was being talked about on a per capita basis. But what we are saying is that energy costs, because of transportation costs and because of our regional dependency on oil, make our prices much higher than prices elsewhere.

The caucus came into being in 1973, and a few months ago Senator Tower made a comment about how much clout we have in New England. I enjoyed hearing that because when we look at energy questions, we do not feel the clout is anywhere near enough.

JUDGE LANGDON: I would like to add just one thing about the Machiasport refinery. At that time, Occidental was looking toward Libya for crude to supply Machiasport. I shudder to think what might have happened economically to the area and to the other people involved if the refinery had been built, because shortly afterwards the Libyans staged their own embargo and the matter was decided, leaving the crude cut off.

MS. SCHUKER: Of course that is true. We ended up having an embargo in any case, and we drained America first without having a New England refinery. I cannot answer what would have happened but, as Judge Langdon says, Libyan crude was cut off. Nevertheless, the lack of the Machiasport refinery isolated New England that much more. Again, we had a drain-America-first situation, and I cannot imagine we could have been much worse off than we ended up last year.

JOHN NASSIKAS, chairman, Federal Power Commission: As the outgoing chairman of the Federal Power Commission, and having wrestled for a little over six years with some of the problems of regulation, I would like to comment briefly on something that everyone has said.

I have advocated the deregulation of new gas supplies to the interstate market, with protective covenants in the public interest for three-and-a-half to four years. I believe this is the only logical way of rationing or allocating our gas resources. Without going in depth into the matter of protective covenants, I might suggest that we need strict antitrust enforcement so that the market itself will remain workably competitive on a national basis. I refer those here to volume one of our *National Gas Survey,* published a few months ago, for an articulate and rational argument why we should have deregulation. We must deregulate new gas supplies so that the interstate market can compete with the intrastate market on a national basis. The U.S. economy is composed of national markets, as Charles Murphy suggests, and should not be fragmented by a congressionally dictated schizoid system of regulation of the interstate market by the Federal Power Commission and nonregulation of the intrastate market by Texas or Oklahoma or Louisiana or Kansas.

We did not develop the capital or the incentives needed to provide inexpensive goods and services to the American public by having parochial markets. One reason why the Republic of Texas has decided not to adopt the radical procedure of dividing into five states, so that Texas might have ten U.S. senators instead of two, is that we then would regulate interstate commerce among those states. And that shows you the wisdom of the Texans.

Secondly, perhaps topically, I would like to address myself to a few matters that Ms. Schuker raised. I applaud some of her comments, and I will take her to task for some of the others. In the first place, New England is a very large beneficiary, for good or ill, of Federal Power Commission regulation. The reason is that our first priority consumers are largely residential and small commercial users who consume less than 50 Mcf per day. New England's consumers are largely first priority consumers. Thus, even though Algonquin and its supplier, Texas Eastern, are in deep curtailment and unable to meet their fixed contract demands, and the Tennessee Gas Transmission Company is also in deep curtailment and unable to meet all contract demands, New England, having a large proportion of first priority consumers, gets no gas cut-offs this winter nor has New England had any gas cut-offs in the history of the Federal Power Commission—at least since I have been chairman of that organization. I would like to set the record straight on that.

Next, it was said—not by Ms. Schuker—that New England is not doing much to protect itself. I would like to say that New England is doing a great deal to try to protect itself. In the first place, for New England to switch around and support the Georges Bank development with all of the opposition to that development that existed three to four years ago is a major accomplishment. I think New Englanders should be applauded for that accomplishment, for getting behind the idea of offshore drilling and developing whatever resources there are offshore New England. These would be developed for New England use, since the point of production would be close to New England.

Another important aspect of New England's attempt to become self-sufficient on barren soil is nuclear power. Barren soil reminds me—it was once remarked that, had the United States been developed from west to east instead of from east to west, New England still would not be discovered. In any case, New England has the highest proportionate concentration of electric power generation by nuclear means of any region in the country. This is important because one nuclear plant of a thousand megawatts or so, at a 60 percent plant factor, would displace about 9 million barrels of oil annually and 2.2 million tons of coal or 55.2 billion cubic feet of natural gas a year. Ten such plants would displace all the natural gas consumed by New England last year. Thus, assuming that uranium will not be in short supply—though we do not have uranium, so far as I know, in the White Mountains of New Hampshire or Vermont's Green Mountains or in the Berkshires of Massachusetts—New England probably will be able to secure its source for power by nuclear means, a point which I think is of vital importance.

One more point, if I may. The price of natural gas delivered to the city gate in Boston ranges from 80 cents to $1.00. The transportation cost has gone up (for many reasons) from two cents to three cents a hundred miles; but one-and-a-half cents per hundred miles is out. The delivered cost of Algerian liquefied natural gas that Distrogas is putting into its terminal in Revere, Massachusetts, runs somewhere between $1.50 and $2.50 a million Btus, on a delivered cost basis, two to three times the cost of natural gas. Going down to Providence, Rhode Island, where there is another terminal on a pending application before the Federal Power Commission, we find that the approximate range of price to deliver Algerian liquefied natural gas to that terminal, when and if certified, would be from $1.50 to $3.00. We have a 100 percent range of cost; it depends on how we can negotiate as U.S. importers with the Algerian government, largely with Soratrach.

There is one other natural gas reforming plant we certified, this one near New Bedford. We certified that gas at $1.99 a million Btus, in a decision over which we anguished for months because of the price. For the output of that plant the price has now escalated to $5.00 a million Btus, compared to the 90 cent to $1.00 price of gas delivered to New England.

In conclusion, I say that it is poor economics, bad public policy, and contrary to the consumer interest to continue gas regulation of new gas supplies by the Federal Power Commission.

MS. SCHUKER: Just a couple of comments on the deregulation of natural gas. My own personal opinion—and the personal opinion of the New England Congressional Caucus economist, Paul Linden—strongly supports the deregulation of natural gas. Privately, and some members of the caucus publicly—Senator Brooke, for one—we have discussed and are supporting deregulation of natural gas. This is a politically difficult issue. As Mr. Nassikas mentioned, the use of natural gas in New England is largely residential; in fact, some 52 percent of the natural gas used in New England is residential and about 18 or 19 percent is industrial. But deregulation, obviously, would hit the people's pocketbooks. Nevertheless the bullet will have to be bitten, and certainly the legislation I mentioned in my speech would address deregulation. I know that senators who are supporting this, including Senator Brooke, have just sent their letter out to their fellow members on this deregulation issue, keying the price of gas on oil. I would think there should be support among New Englanders on this, but I cannot give any kind of prospective tally.

There was one other point I would like to comment on. Mr. Nassikas said there were no natural gas cut-offs and although I do not think I have touched on that in what I said, I am aware of it. This point about New Englanders' doing much to protect themselves did not include our work in Congress. The delegation, and the governors as well, has supported the Coastal Zone Management Program on the development of offshore oil, a program that provides for a large state role in any kind of exploration or drilling. Given the safeguards built into that program (and we have been supporting some new amendments to it), the possibility of offshore development is becoming much greater than it has been.

GOVERNOR DUKAKIS: I am not sure that ancient history is particularly valuable, but some of this is not so ancient, is it? I hope New Englanders will be pardoned a bit if they react with blunt and sometimes sectional responses to this problem, at least in the short run, as they try to cope with all the serious economic problems brought to their doorstep. I think it is fair to say that in two important respects New Englanders were the victims of nonmarket government-imposed and artificially inflated prices. First, the import quota program, no matter how it was taken, meant that the country was not taking advantage of those international forces Mr. Murphy talked about, which would have not only provided oil prices substantially lower than what New England had to pay, but would have permitted New England to develop its own refineries—and not only develop them, but keep the refinery that already was in operation. We had a small refinery about seven miles from Boston, Massachusetts, and there were serious plans for additional refining capacity in Rhode Island, which were destroyed by the quota program in 1959. It was that playing with the price in the interest of the producing states—or perhaps in the national interest—that created a great many of our difficulties in the 1950s and 1960s and early 1970s.

Second, the unilateral imposition by the President of a tariff hurt New England badly, in part because the Congress would not accept the rest of the President's program. This again was done by government action, presumably in the national interest, but in a way that unquestionably hit us disproportionately to the rest of the country.

What I am saying is that, while New England proceeds with resource development in what we hope is a balanced and sensible way—and I think we will be learning from the experience of Texas and Louisiana as we proceed on outer continental shelf development—I hope others will bear in mind that these two government-imposed policies, which have been directly contrary to some of the things I have been told here were in the national interest, have had a very serious effect on us.

23

The fact that we had to cope with them and were hurt by them has obviously had a significant effect on our present situation. I hope we will be pardoned if we react in kind, even though many will think that is not a good idea. As we come out of this and begin to get our feet on the ground and get our bearings, I think there will be a somewhat more balanced and mature New England approach to this, an approach which leaves some of our early paranoia behind. But though we will leave it behind, it is a paranoia which, I suggest, was justified under the circumstances.

LLOYD UNSELL, Independent Petroleum Association of America: I would just like to say that this conclusion about the oil import program's imposing unfair cost is certainly subject to debate. I will just take Ms. Schuker's time frame of the 1960s, which was the principal time the import program was in effect. The argument that the program was used to hold domestic prices up is certainly not borne out by the facts, because under successive administrations, Democratic and Republican alike, every minimal increase in domestic crude oil prices was jumped on by the administration.

The result was that, when we convert domestic natural gas prices to crude-oil equivalent and average oil and gas prices, we find that the real price of domestic oil and natural gas (in 1974 dollars) declined from $3.06 a barrel to $2.48 a barrel from 1960 to 1970. Ms. Schuker mentioned, I believe, that the prices for petroleum fuels in New England went down 20 cents in the 1960s, and indeed the price of domestic oil and gas went down in real terms. She also said that the producing states constantly have argued for higher prices: I think this is debatable. I think domestic independent oil and natural gas producers certainly have argued for free-market prices—but free-market prices, historically, have not meant higher prices; historically, they have meant lower prices. Because for a hundred years in this country, before the federal government began setting prices, the relative prices of oil and natural gas in the United States were consistently below the prices of commodities generally in this country.

Charles Murphy, of course, agrees with the New England contingent that the import program was a mistake. However, I say it was a mistake only because, under successive administrations, it was used to hold domestic oil and gas prices down artificially, rather than to prop them up. I also contend—and I do not believe there are many economists in the country who would disagree—that if there had been free-market prices for domestic oil and natural gas through this period, rather than price by government coercion in the case of crude and direct controls at the wellhead in the case of natural gas, we would not have had the supply problem we have now.

In the 1960s because of the cost-price squeeze, we deactivated, dismantled, and junked 60 percent of the rotary drilling rigs in this country. We shoved 72,000 skilled workers out of the domestic oil and gas industry and put them into other enterprises, and we lost about half the independent natural gas producers and oil producers in this country. And this is why we have an energy crisis.

W. T. BLACKBURN, Vaughey and Vaughey: I am an independent producer of oil and gas, and have been for thirty-five years. I have no regional bias, no feel for one region against another, just so long as they use the same currency. I have gas production in western Canada and property in Toronto, so I have to be neutral there, too. Dr. Russell has pointed out that the two problems, oil and gas, should be separated: I am inclined to agree with him. I am inclined to talk more about natural gas because I like to win arguments and that is what I know most about.

I would disagree with Dr. Russell when he says there is not enough natural gas to go around. But some of the peculiarities of the natural gas business are very peculiar. I am producing gas that I have produced for twenty years, and I am selling it for 21 cents per thousand cubic feet. I do not know where it is going, but I hope it is going to New England because it is quite a bargain. I am also producing gas and selling it in the intrastate market at a dollar a thousand cubic feet, and I am not making much. I believe that the answer is really simple.

There is gas, for instance, in Colorado in the Piceance Basin that cannot be produced at present prices, and there is a considerable amount of it. But this gas can be produced, and though I do not know what price it will take to produce it, the price is more than can be realized now in either the interstate or intrastate market. Whether the market will absorb this gas when it is produced depends completely on where the market falls in the event of deregulation. If the gas should not be produced, it will not be: the marketplace will control it. We can have so much gas at 65 cents, we can have more at 75 cents, we can have more at $1.00, we can have more at $1.50. But there is no philanthrophic justification for drilling gas, only the profit justification: I think that deregulation will be a good thing for all regions of the country.

GOVERNOR BOREN: One of the problems that we have when we talk about natural gas pricing—I had a lengthy discussion with Senator Hollings last night on this same point—is the failure to make a distinction between the average price of natural gas paid in this country and the new price. There is a big difference between the two. I am looking here at the New England caucus position. The caucus talks about one approach which would be inflationary, and that would be to let the price of natural gas rise to the equivalent of the world price of oil, about $13.50 a barrel. No one is talking about letting the average price of natural gas in this country go to that level. Even if we let new gas go to that level, the average price would still be a small fraction of that.

What we tried to do in the White House Conference was overcome regional feelings, as we did in the Midwestern Governors' Conference and in the Southern conference, where we have states like North Carolina that are very hard-hit. We have had thirty-one governors express support for a plan that would suspend all regulations on natural gas—not a phased deregulation, but suspension of all regulations for a period of five years. In other words, new wells drilled during that period would be forever decontrolled, and the price negotiated during that period would be the price. The inflationary effect of this decontrol on the average price of natural gas—which is the important thing to the consumer, not the price for new gas necessarily but the average price—will, we think, be very small.

I have pointed to the Oklahoma example, to the fact that while our price for new gas has risen in the intrastate market, the average price for all gas still has not risen very much: the residential user of natural gas in Oklahoma has only experienced a 4.8 percent per year increase in utility bills. Let me point out why I think the five-year plan makes a lot of sense for all regions, since the governor of Massachusetts or a congressman from Massachusetts, for example, cannot afford to be for a plan that may have a wild inflationary impact upon his consumers. But if there is a five-year cap on the program, there is no way that the average price of gas can rise rapidly enough to hurt the consumer.

One question is, if there is five-year gradual decontrol, what are the producer and the investor going to do? They may hope that when the five years are up, decontrol will be extended and we will have full decontrol, but they do not know. They are going to put as much capital into exploring for new wells as they possibly can during the five-year period, and that capital investment will have a maximum impact on the discovery of new gas. We can get the new gas right into the pipeline: I should emphasize that one good thing about gas is that we have a pipeline delivery system. The minute the well comes onstream, we can get the gas delivered.

For the short-term crisis, I think this five-year plan makes a lot of sense. I want to make one other brief point. Our interstate energy council commissioned the Arthur Young Company to study utility bills in New York City, for the Brooklyn Union Gas Company. We found that the company's residential consumers were paying $2.60 a unit, and out of that $2.60 a unit, twenty-five cents went to the producer in Oklahoma at the wellhead. This is the average wellhead price of natural gas that they were paying, twenty-five cents. (They had a lot of old contracts.) The pipeline company was getting about sixty cents, the distribution cost once the gas got to New York was $1.75. The total came to $2.60 to the consumer.

Now, under a five-year suspension program, that average price of twenty-five cents is not going to go up much. What about the pipeline cost? Amortizing $30 billion worth of pipelines costs the consumers in the East a lot of money. And when the pipeline is run half-full, the average amortization per unit the consumer has to pay is higher than it would be if the pipeline were run full. The pipeline cost was twice as much as what the producer in Oklahoma was getting for his gas. If those pipelines can be run full, the amortization cost will be less, which will cut a little bit of the cost to the consumer.

Overall, I think gradual decontrol would encourage an adequate supply, with protection for the consumer, and encouragement for maximum production within five years. I think it is something we could live with in different parts of the country—indeed I think it would be beneficial. But Senator Hollings says, "We will just peg it all at the average price, $1.30." The problem is that we need to discover new gas at depths below 15,000 feet, and the cost of getting that gas is higher than $1.30. So, if we are going to get new gas below 15,000 feet, we must let the new price go up. But to do that will not, if we put a cap on it, raise the average price very much. I sincerely believe that we can decontrol. I have no pride of authorship in this plan, but it is something that thirty-one governors from different regions of the country have been able to come together on, and I think it shows there is a glimmer of hope that we can find a national approach.

MR. RUSSELL: I would like to comment on what was said by the last two speakers. First, since I am on record in a number of places as believing that the natural gas shortage was due to regulation, it comes as quite a shock to me to hear that I said there was not enough natural gas to go around. I think I was saying there was not enough to go around in the regulated markets and the interstate markets. But that brings us to a second point that I think Governor Boren commented on when he was talking about the higher gas prices necessary to elicit supply. Certainly, higher gas prices will elicit supply in the short run, though, of course, there will be some time lags: more important, though, is our focusing on the other side of the issue.

One of the reasons we need higher prices for gas—and I would argue that we need them even though consumers never like higher prices of anything—is so that we will use the gas we do have more efficiently. We do not like to recognize the fact that one impact of higher gas prices is that some consumers, perhaps in those producing regions, are going to find it uneconomic to continue burning gas under boilers. And consequently, I would suggest that one of our goals would be to have prices high enough to ration the available supply among those consumers with the greatest demands. It is appealing to talk about higher gas prices as though there were an infinite pool of gas that would immediately be brought on the market, but I think we must recognize that the world of energy prices has changed over the last five years. It changed as dramatically as it did because of the OPEC price increase, but it was changing long before, and it will continue to change if OPEC prices disappear.

We must adjust to these higher energy prices, and one way to adjust is to start using energy more efficiently than we have, which means using it differently from the way we have been. Certainly using natural gas, a premium fuel, in some of the ways it is now being used under that average base price of 20 cents in the field does not carry over those rational allocations we all recognize we need.

GOVERNOR DUKAKIS: Let me say this: I think there is a certain kind of eternal contradiction here. Governor Boren is arguing for a modest step in the direction of deregulation, which really would not have much effect on the average price. I wonder—and this is not an argument against that policy—if in fact it does have only a very modest effect on the average price, would the kinds of results which Mr. Russell has been talking about really come about, since I gather the average price would still be substantially cheaper than the average price of other fuels.

GOVERNOR BOREN: I certainly agree with the point Mr. Russell is making here. Philosophically, I believe in total deregulation, allowing the price of all units of natural gas to reach parity with oil and other fuels. Now, that is what I believe philosophically. We have a scarce and precious natural resource, and when we keep the price of that resource down at 12 or 20 cents, we encourage people to use it uneconomically and wastefully. But over and above that, there is the political problem we have to face, though I find the political problem greater in talking with members of Congress than I do in talking with the governors. I think congressmen simply perceive a pressure from the consumers in their state and think, "My goodness, if the price goes up too fast to this industrial or residential user of a utility, decontrol will be a problem of political longevity as well as an energy solution."

I, being from a producing state, can nevertheless sympathize with those who have those fears for their political longevity. If we had only to adopt a pure philosophical approach and do what I think is right, I would certainly agree with what Mr. Russell is saying. But I would say that, being politically realistic, and trying to get us off dead center, we must do something that protects against the average prices' rising too much. What we do will mask some of the effects that we have been discussing.

I would say that we are moving—and I think any industry would be foolish not to move—toward alternate sources of fuel. For example, the degree of boiler use of natural gas in Oklahoma where it has been plentiful and frozen in under old contracts is being changed as rapidly as we can change it. Every utility I know of in the state of Oklahoma is moving to alternate sources right now because of uncertainty and because of the realization that we are dealing with a scarce commodity. I admit our five-year compromise is not perfection, but it is something that would be a lot better than what we have now. It might be politically possible for all regions of the country to get together on this. It does admittedly sacrifice some of the elements of conservation, and perhaps we can figure out other ways and substitutes other than price for preventing wasteful use of natural gas.

A. V. JONES, Jones Company, Ltd.: I would like to expand a little bit on what the governor of Oklahoma said. The raising of prices to assure supply is a practical

28

reality. It has happened in Texas. While New England was getting along very well without any curtailment, Texas was under considerable curtailment. The University of Texas at Austin had to shut down because the buildings were not warm enough for the students to go to school in. But this year intrastate gas prices rose enough to entice investment into the business and I think the new prices have substantially alleviated that shortage. In fact, we are going to be in good shape this winter throughout the state of Texas. So, we have cases at hand of the response of supply to price. We did not lose the entire domestic oil industry during the 1960s. We do have the capacity and the ability, if the economic incentive is there, to bring on gas for the whole nation.

MARTIN MILLER, chairman, Vermont Public Utility Commission: In Vermont we buy our natural gas from Canada, and of course we have been paying the Canadian price, which is unregulated. The Canadians have made no bones about it: they expect the price of gas to reach parity with oil in two years. This has had an obvious undesirable short-term effect, but in the long run, people will be able to choose with some certainty as to what will be. Ms. Schuker is, I think, short-sighted in not discussing the third part of what I consider the energy problem, which is electricity. The major builders are saying, "We cannot depend on energy. We are going to lose our investment. We are going to let the utilities worry about it, and we are going to put up our major buildings and heat them and run them by electricity." Economics 101 teaches us that since we need some form of energy, the consumers are going to be hurt unless the energy used is what is most efficient for the region. I seriously question whether it is in New England's interest in the long run even to think about oil as an important ingredient in its economy. The fact that industry has left New England has changed the character of New England. Recognizing the problems of stability in any pricing structure, we should ask why the oil industry does not agree that the price controls that we now have should be phased out over a period of time, so that we will have the opportunity to go to the alternate sources which we are trying to develop, including getting the offshore oil in New England. Perhaps Mr. Murphy could answer me.

MR. MURPHY: I think that the majority of the oil companies have espoused precisely that program, Mr. Miller. As a matter of fact, we have done so to such an extent that Mr. Royster's newspaper has chided us for not sticking to basic principles. We have done this—and it certainly has been my company's recommendation to the Congress and the administration—because we believe it is a realistic course of action. Let me be absolutely frank. One reason is business longevity: in Washington there is a punitive attitude toward the oil companies. I do not think the price of oil would go up abruptly if controls were removed. I agree with the *Wall Street Journal* editorials that competition would take care of the price. But we are afraid that if we were wrong and the price did shoot up and stay up, punitive legislation would be pushed and pushed—divorcement and all the rest of the litany.

The other thing is, perhaps, a little less in the line of self-interest. We believe in the free market, and yet the price of oil has been held down for a long time, and it was the abrupt increase in the price that took place beginning in the fall of 1973—not the absolute price level—that has really wrenched the economy of the country and of the world. It was the abrupt nature of the increase. And, as Professor Mitchell has put it, a period of decompression may be in order—the shorter the better. But for those two reasons, political and macroeconomic, my company and most of the integrated companies whose policy statements I have read are doing exactly what Mr. Miller suggests we should do.

My final point is really a question for Ms. Schuker, because I thought that in the last paragraph of her paper she was trying to throw out an olive branch, when she talked about the energy meeting being held at Martha's Vineyard, and she referred to a paper for this meeting written by the Boston Federal Reserve Bank's chief economists, Robert Eisenmenger and Richard Syron making the point that "the region's competitive position is determined not by the absolute price of oil but by the price of oil relative to other fuels." I thought the principal thrust of what Dr. Russell was saying was that one of the ways that you can ensure equal pricing was through decontrol, and I think any economist would agree to that. Ms. Schuker goes on to say, "I think this is the crucial point which needs further exploration. . . ." The way I read that, Ms. Schuker really favors decontrol.

MS. SCHUKER: First, the Federal Reserve Bank of Boston and its economists do favor decontrol. Many of the regional economists in New England favor decontrol. I mentioned earlier that an economist at the New England Economic Research Office who works with the congressional caucus office here has been strongly advocating the decontrol of natural gas and has come a long way toward convincing me. At the moment it is doubtful that he has convinced all the members of the delegation. I was making that point when I said that the issue is to key the price of oil on the differential from the cost of other fuels, gas being one.

However, I used the term "political hot potato." This is an issue that I think some have privately come a long way on: whether their coming a long way is going to show publicly in votes, whether they would be interested in the "re-regulation" idea floating around on the Hill is something else, but the arguments make sense to me. But then again, someone mentioned the term "political longevity," and I am not going home to run. I think this is a critical issue. When it comes to public opinion, our elected officials are the ones who have to bite the bullet. I am not speaking, as I said, for the New England Congressional Caucus in the sense of putting them on record in support of decontrol of natural gas, but decontrol certainly makes a lot of sense.

PART TWO

Energy Self-Sufficiency for the United States

At the luncheon session Vice President Nelson Rockefeller spoke of an energy corporation that would serve as the catalyst needed to translate scientific and technological advances into energy self-sufficiency for the United States. This corporation would provide the initial capital investments for energy development by private enterprise, investments which would be repaid by private enterprise after ten years, when they began to yield a return. It would also act as a central clearing house for all federal, state, and local regulations on energy developments in which it was a participant.

ENERGY SELF-SUFFICIENCY FOR THE UNITED STATES: THE ENERGY CORPORATION

Nelson Rockefeller

To all of you in this national conference, I would like to say thanks for letting me be with you. Let me briefly outline our current situation and the proposed Energy Independence Authority—a program which grew out of the realities of the times in which we live.

This country, for many years, was an energy exporter, self-sufficient and dynamic. Then, as we grew, and as our consumption of energy increased, we became importers, and then net importers, and then dependent on imports. The other producing nations joined together a good many years ago in the Organization of Petroleum Exporting Countries (OPEC) and made a few attempts to raise prices, but they were unable to succeed in raising prices until we found ourselves in a net importing position. Then, with the blow-up in the Middle East, which acted as a catalyst for dramatic action by the OPEC countries (led by the Arab countries as part of the overall Middle East political situation), we saw the embargo and the 500 percent increase in oil prices in a period of two years. These events changed the world situation for both the industrial nations and the developing nations.

Last fall President Ford spent considerable time studying the situation, with a series of meetings on economics and energy, and then came up with a comprehensive legislative program outlined in his State of the Union message. This program is based on the idea that this country must—for national security reasons, for the strength and vitality of our economy, for the reactivation of economic growth—become self-sufficient in energy by 1985.

What I think has been generally overlooked is the fact that energy has traditionally been a free enterprise operation, a free-market operation, as far as the United States government is concerned. And that free market has not been limited to the domestic area: it has operated internationally. But the minute the President declared a national policy for self-sufficiency, he cut across the basic free-market structure. Our government has not traditionally had the kind of relationships with private enterprise that countries like Japan have developed, where labor, industry, finance, and government are expected to work together. These countries do not have the same kind of antitrust problems we do, and we therefore have a situation totally different from theirs. Congress was faced with a difficult

33

problem: how to treat this question with international prices rising rapidly, domestic production held to a fixed price and a net decline in production.

During the past ten months there has been no evident response by the Congress in any form commensurate with the urgency and scale of the problem we face as a nation. Let us face it: it is a difficult problem, complex, with many unattractive features. Becoming self-sufficient involves high costs, which are extremely unattractive, particularly when we are looking forward to an election year. Consequently, there has been no effective action taken and here we are, two years after the boycott, and instead of being "somewhat" dependent on imported oil, almost 40 percent dependent on it, spending almost $26 billion a year in imports—money out of this country, money that could be used for employment in a period when we have high unemployment. Now there is a new 10 percent increase that will lead to our spending another $2.6 billion, bringing us close to $30 billion a year.

Looking at the good side of the picture, we can see that this country is blessed with unusual natural resources. We have in shale oil alone twice as much oil as the Middle East has in known reserves. We have five times as much coal as we have oil, and then there is the potential for extraordinary amounts of energy produced through atomic power plants. Natural gas is an important area but one where the government has been regulating for years. Natural gas is obviously the most desirable fuel of all for home or industry, and by government regulation it is the cheapest. Unfortunately, at present prices, it does not pay the producers to produce the quantities that are necessary, and our production is therefore falling off. Rationing has come in, and if we have a cold winter, we are going to have an extremely serious situation, resulting in even higher unemployment in a dozen or eighteen states in this country that depend heavily on gas.

We have a number of complex problems. Let me draw a parallel. There was an interesting case, I remember, with rubber during World War II. I happened to be here in Washington and was a close friend of Jesse Jones. He was active in trying to preserve the Western Hemisphere sea lanes that provided for the flow of rubber from the Amazon basin, which was the last place we could get it. The government, through the RFC, established what was known as the Rubber Reserve Corporation. This corporation contracted with private groups to develop synthetic rubber, and five or six of the processes developed proved to be successful. The government then sold the processes. In this case the government was the catalyst and there was no expense to the taxpayer. Thus, the nation became self-sufficient in synthetic rubber.

Now, the Energy Research and Development Administration (ERDA) is doing research in fuels. It is developing in laboratories a wide range of potential sources, right across the board—fossil fuels and atomic—but it does not have the authorization or the funds to translate these into commercial production. Translating laboratory work into commercial production is rather expensive and quite risky. If one does not know what the price is, he is faced with a difficult situation. Under the present regulations, free enterprise has not been willing to invest the necessary money to develop these new sources of energy production, and to meet the co-equal requirements in relation to ecology. I am confident that we can meet our energy requirements and our ecological requirements together but it will take research and capital investment and there is risk involved. The idea behind the Energy Independence Authority is to accelerate the whole experimental operation, translating scientific and technical knowledge into commercial production, so as to accelerate the independence of this country in energy supply.

Let me give a few illustrations of the kind of thing that can be done. If it were possible to produce oil from oil shale by drilling down, putting off an explosion, setting the oil shale on fire, taking the gas that was then formed out by pipe and condensing it, if that could be done (as is estimated by the Livermore Laboratories) at a price between seven and eight dollars a barrel, we would be home free for a long time to come in oil. But it is, at least, a $200 million experiment and no one is willing to risk this investment. Occidental has done work in this field but no firms are willing to go the whole way on their own.

The same is true for gas from coal using the same process. The cost could possibly be in the same range, whereas if we make gas from coal after mining the coal, the cost runs as high as a $24.00 a barrel equivalent, while liquefied gas is even more. These experiments need to be carried out commercially in the gas, coal, and oil fields. If we move over into atomic energy, we find that some 70 percent of the planned atomic plants have been deferred or cancelled.

The President said, in his message in January, that he wanted 200 new atomic power plants. As I say, 70 percent of those under consideration have been cancelled. One reason for the cancellations is the risk involved in the capital expenditure. Part of the problem is that if a company invests a billion dollars, which is approximately what a big plant costs, it cannot get these expenditures in its rate base until the plant is on-line. With the new ecological requirements—the filing of impact statements and so on—bringing the plant on-line is now an eleven-year process rather than a four-year process. To tie up a billion dollars until the plant is on-line eleven years later is an impossibility for most companies.

Here again, this energy corporation, on a self-liquidating basis, could build nuclear power plants and sell them on lease/purchase agreements over a period of years. In this manner, after nine to eleven years, we would have all the electric energy we required. And of course we cannot run an economy, an industrial economy, without adequate energy. We cannot have new jobs without adequate energy. This energy corporation would really be a stimulant to the private sector to meet the needs of the country, domestically, out of our own resources. The President has set the goal, and the capital investment estimated to achieve this goal is between $600 billion and $800 billion in the next ten years, out of a total capital investment requirement estimated for the nation, in all areas, of about $4 trillion.

I think that this will act as the catalyst necessary to get our country off dead-center. If we get the energy program off dead-center, with energy and ecology going hand in hand, it will help get the economy, as a whole, off dead-center and really rolling. This will create the opportunity for employment, the restoration of strength, the opportunity for production of goods and services that are necessary to meet our ecological needs, to restore what nature has given us, to provide the jobs people want, and to fulfill our responsibilities in the world.

It is a large amount—that is true—but it is about 10 percent of our projected total capital investment over these years. When people talk about the problem of diverting capital from other sources through government channeling of capital, they must realize this has already been set as national policy. It was set when the President declared this as his objective. I do not think I need to say much more about energy development except to answer questions. This should be an exciting moment in the history of this country. I believe we must rethink a great many things in order to preserve the strength and vitality of democracy. We must provide opportunity for our people as free citizens, which is the heritage that we have been so fortunate to have had for the past 200 years, so that we will have the vitality in the next 200 years that we have enjoyed in the past.

As far as the chance of passage of the program is concerned, I think labor is very enthusiastic and that has some relation to what the Congress does. Industry, I think, is growing desperate for energy, particularly those in industry who are worried about natural gas. Now I was at a midwestern governors' meeting and Governor Exon of Nebraska said "I don't think anyone really believes there is an energy crisis: there is plenty of oil around." And I said, "Well, you have summarized it right there. Sure, there is plenty of oil around because we are importing it, but the fact that we are importing it is the basis of the crisis."

If our oil imports are cut off, we will be in a bad position indeed. Those of us who live on the East Coast are now between 80 and 90 percent dependent on imported oil. If another war broke out in the Middle East, and things really got out of hand, I think we could see chaos on the whole Eastern seaboard. We went through a taste of it before, but it was only a very small taste.

In industry, there are some who are opposed to this energy corporation on the ground that this is capital allocation by government. There are others who are opposed to any government intervention in the market. There are others who say this would be the first step to a takeover by government, a first step toward socialization. I think the only way our system is going to work is for us to go on with research and development and the application of research and development to meet the needs of our people. The risk is so great here in this interim period that private enterprise is hesitant to make the investments which are essential for our national interest.

When President Roosevelt said at the beginning of World War II, "We are going to have 60,000 planes," everyone thought he was crazy. We ended up producing 124,000 planes. This country can do anything it sets its mind to. We have the resources; we have the capability; we have the technical knowledge; we have the scientists. We must combine them. Government's role is to meet the needs of the people that they cannot meet for themselves, or to see that they are met, and this is one of the needs that they are not meeting for themselves. This program would be established on a self-liquidating limited basis for a period of seven years. After that, no new commitments would be made.

My personal belief is that this proposal will be well received when it is understood and when the alternatives are seen. Also, I think that the employment facet would be very significant. At the same time, it would not add to the budget deficit, which is the problem that the President is facing in trying to hold down inflation.

QUESTIONS AND ANSWERS

ENDICOTT PEABODY, Americans for Energy Independence: Mr. Vice President, you compared the situation today to the situation before and during World War II when we found we could build 120,000 planes. But before Pearl Harbor we found we had trouble building tanks and planes. We then found that the answer was something like the War Production Board that Pearl Harbor had created. Right now we have a number of disparate agencies, some in the energy field, some in the environmental field, all competing with one another, and the poor person who is constructing an energy plant is bedeviled by one side or another. Now, what is the solution to this?

VICE PRESIDENT ROCKEFELLER: This law or, more properly, this program calls for the agency to act as a clearing house for all regulatory agencies on any project in which the government is a participant. The agency would be a participant only if private capital were insufficient, but it would also be available for those projects that would contribute to national independence, to act as a clearing house for government regulations. The agency would be in a position to make recommendations for legislative changes to facilitate both the social objectives for which the regulations were created and an acceleration in the speed with which the job would be done. The present inordinate delays create uncertainties that are part of the problem.

One reason these developments are not being carried out is that people, if they invest $100 million on the basis of present calculations, present rules and regulations, do not know whether these will be changed and their ability to make a profit destroyed later on. Under these circumstances the tendency is not to make any commitment.

DAVID HOWELL, Community Planning Resources: Some economists are not as enthusiastic about your plan as apparently labor and industry are, and some critics have suggested that your off-budget financing has played a not insignificant role in the plight of New York today. How do you deal with this kind of criticism in this context?

VICE PRESIDENT ROCKEFELLER: I think success will depend on good management, to be perfectly honest. We cannot run anything, even a Swiss watch, unless we understand how it works and how to handle it. What you are referring to is the Urban Development Corporation. The Urban Development Corporation produced, or is completing, 30,000 units of housing in the state, housing desperately needed, and it produced the housing in record time. UDC had a cash flow problem, which resulted from the lack of implementation of its financial plan. There was a change of administration between Governor Wilson and Governor Carey, from one party to the other. As a result, $200 million of obligations, which were part of the plan, were not purchased. I have to believe that when the new governor came in, he had not had much experience in New York's problems, and because this was an organization, created by a previous administration, and because it looked like it was going to have trouble, he thought that not purchasing the obligations might be a political plus. What I think he realizes now is that this was the start of what turned out to be a very serious political minus. UDC has now completed the sale of its long-term bonds and is in perfect shape and is back on its feet because its credit was good.

If we set up something that is complicated, we must have people who understand it and who have the ability to manage it. But I think government's function is to do those things for people that they cannot do for themselves and that are necessary to preserve the system.

LES GAPAY, *Wall Street Journal*: Mr. Vice President, would this corporation have the authority to relax environmental restrictions on these projects?

VICE PRESIDENT ROCKEFELLER: No, sir.

KIT JOHNSTON, *Oilgram News*: How would you respond to a charge that this government support would, in all likelihood, go to many of the major energy companies who have developed domestic resources in the past? How would you respond to a charge that this kind of government support to them for essential development is unconscionable because they have not provided us with a good standing ground now?

VICE PRESIDENT ROCKEFELLER: This goes to the question of whether we believe in the free enterprise system. If we believe in it and we expect the energy companies to produce, and if the risks are too great for them to make the necessary investment, then the government must step in and provide incentives. However, if we believe in socialism, we might say, "Well, the government should take the whole thing over." I do not think we have done very well in the management of things taken over by government. When the government starts out, it always

40

thinks matters are going to be very simple. When the government gets into them, as with the railroads, they become more complicated in a hurry.

This country has chosen to buy its military equipment through private enterprise rather than by setting up a government military production complex. The same argument could be made there: why should the government not manufacture airplanes or guns itself instead of contracting with private companies? And this, really, is exactly the same thing. It would be contracting with private groups to accomplish an objective that is in the national interest.

STAN BENJAMIN, United Press International: Mr. Vice President, from a practical point of view how would you go about deciding which companies actually cannot make the investments themselves and which companies simply might be seeking to have government subsidize the highest risk part of the venture?

VICE PRESIDENT ROCKEFELLER: That is a good question and the answer depends on the capability of management. There would be two criteria for our decision: first, would the program contribute to self-sufficiency or independence in energy production and, second, could it be financed by private capital? The answer to the first would have to be "yes" and the answer to the second "no," and then the project would have to be self-liquidating to the maximum degree possible.

There is some risk here, but it should be remembered that the project will have to be sold afterwards to the highest bidder, which might be an existing company or it might be a group of private investors joined together to buy it. If we talk to the people who are involved, we can find out pretty quickly why something was not built. The truth of the matter is that we are losing ground so far as self-sufficiency is concerned rather than gaining it. We are vulnerable as a nation from a security point of view as a result of our position, and we are subject to blackmail because of the vulnerability.

ROBERT CAHN, The Conservation Foundation: Mr. Vice President, there are two phases to the shortage. One is supply and the other is demand. Do you have any plan coming up for energy conservation?

VICE PRESIDENT ROCKEFELLER: Yes. The President has sent recommendations to the Congress for legislation that would encourage energy conservation by giving tax deductions to homeowners who put insulation in their homes, for low-income families, actually subsidizing insulation with a whole series of complex legislative actions. This particular corporation also has a function in this area. For instance, if we mine shale that has oil in it and take the oil out, we have what I call talcum powder. There is no water in the shale areas, or very little. What do we do with the talcum powder? If we put it in a valley, a strong wind will blow it out, and that is a serious ecological and environmental problem. However, if we

take the oil out underground, then we have no environmental problem, and this is
the kind of thing I think has to be taken into consideration. The same is true of
coal. We ought to be able to gasify coal or carry out the liquefaction of coal
underground, thereby preventing a lot of environmental problems. There are great
opportunities here but no one is yet willing to take the risks involved. I think it is
the role of government to take some risks for the benefit of the people in the
broadest sense of the word.

PART THREE

Producers and Consumers

The participants in the afternoon session agreed that while the energy problem is one of great complexity, it is still capable of being solved through the political processes of reconciliation and compromise, provided the American people learn that the problem is real and its solution vital for the national interest. Every region contains both producers and consumers, and no solution can promote the exclusive interests of either group. There was widespread support for a solution based upon the market mechanism, but with special consideration given to the problems of particular consumers and regions.

THE POLITICS OF RECONCILIATION BETWEEN PRODUCER AND CONSUMER INTERESTS

Pete V. Domenici

My reaction on learning of the topic assigned to me was that I would have preferred almost any other topic because of the complexities involved in the political reconciliation between producer and consumer interests. On reflection, however, I am impressed with the fact that the reluctance of politicians to address difficult issues in an objective manner is one of the major reasons for our country's current energy nightmare. Accordingly, I am pleased to discuss with you this afternoon some of the thoughts that have occurred to me as I have tried to do my job as a United States senator in reconciling consumer and producer interests.

Perhaps it is appropriate that you bring in a freshman senator, two years and eight months in the Senate, one who really has no legislative experience, to talk on this subject of political reconciliation. At least I do not bring to the arena the ordinary kind of political bias or a long history of balancing legislative pros and cons. I hope I come instead with the commitment to solve our problems.

It seems to me that the reconciliation we are looking for is a must. You may have chosen me as a senator who comes from a producing state. But most of its people do not live where the production is and do not have any interest in it. In any case, as I look over the last two years, it seems to me that we have a very simple proposition for the American people in any state.

From the outset, my ability, and indeed my intention, to try to help reconcile those differences is suspect, because I do represent a producing state. New Mexico in 1974 was the fourth largest producer of natural gas and the sixth largest producer of oil among all the states. So, on this issue I am subject to extremely close scrutiny on the grounds of bias toward producer interests.

National legislators have a bias to overcome on most important issues because they are elected by a state or district that usually has an accepted point of view on those issues. Not unreasonably, then, the legislator finds himself, perhaps as his first impulse, determining the benefit or detriment to his constituency flowing from the various positions that can be taken on each issue.

On the issue of energy, as I find is the case with most important issues, we have a complex set of interests within the context of which a legislator must work and from which he feels he must choose the interest most deserving his support or protection. The very theme of this conference suggests one set of competing interests—national interests and regional interests. The next logical classification in

45

competing energy interests is at the regional level between energy-producing and energy-consuming areas of the country, the topic of my talk. Finally, superimposed over these interests, which are difficult enough in themselves, is the interest each one of us and each constituent of every elected official shares—we are all consumers of energy.

How is a conscientious politician to reconcile these seemingly diametrically opposed competing interests and have any political credibility? That question and its lack of a satisfactory answer lie at the heart of the congressional inability to address our energy problems with anything resembling a national policy or program. This is a distressing situation and I admit to discouragement and frustration in dealing with it myself, but I think there are several fundamental points that can be built on in generating the political climate necessary for the reconciliation of the competing interests, in order to promote the national interest.

When a politician starts to make noises about "the national interest" or the "country's well-being" his audience begins to fret, yawns become hard to stifle and, before long, eyes commence to glaze. In short, those words, "national interest," have been so misused through the years that just to utter them is to have one's sincerity called into question. Understandably, there is a tendency either for the politician to downplay the national interest theme or for his audience to tune him out when he drapes himself in the flag in order to justify action detrimental to the recipient of his bad tidings. That is a harsh statement and, if it is true, as I fear, it is a sad commentary on our national conscience and consciousness.

It was not always so, for when Alexis de Tocqueville wrote of his perceptions of the United States and its political system, he noted that

> in the United States, the interests of the country are everywhere kept in view; they are an object of solicitude to the people of the whole Union, and every citizen is as warmly attached to them as if they were his own. He takes pride in the glory of his Nation; he boasts of its success, to which he conceives himself to have contributed; and he rejoices by the general prosperity by which he profits. The feeling he entertains toward the State, is analogous to that which unites him to his family, and it is by a kind of selfishness that he interests himself in the welfare of his country.

That seems to say that in 1830 Americans recognized that through our system, with its downward flow of benefits, the individual was bound to improve his own lot by contributing to the common good. I am convinced that, although the motivation of our citizens toward promoting the public interest has decreased and their inclination to look solely to their own direct interests has increased, they will still respond when convinced of a genuine national need.

I believe that the most effective way to reconcile the major differences between consumer and producer interests is to subjugate both to the pursuit of the national interest, treating each as fairly as possible in that pursuit. In order to set the stage for such an attitude, the true national interest must be identified, agreed to generally, and promoted throughout the land, regenerating the mood of individual

46

willingness to contribute to the common good that impressed Tocqueville. Although I am concerned about the American people's feeling for this country, and about its politicians' lack of dedication to the nation's needs, I still believe that if the truth about our national energy situation were fully realized, we could pursue an agreed-on course in the public interest.

Let me explain one of the difficulties this way. A visit home to New Mexico six weeks ago put me in the position of talking to eight different crowds of 100 people or more, and regardless of my subject, I decided in each event to assure them that I did not care how they voted, but I would like them to put up their hands if they thought there was an energy crisis in the United States. The results were amazing. Here I come from a fairly sophisticated state politically. It is a producing state and it has good media coverage, and I was thoroughly and utterly amazed—with production-oriented senators and congressmen speaking to these constituents over and over—that only 50 to 55 percent of the people raised their hands in response to that simple question, "Do we have an energy crisis?"

A basic premise of reconciliation is that all of us combined, the legislators who represent consumers and those who represent producers (though we are talking about these two groups as if they were easily defined, which they are not), have done a deplorable job even of building an arena for reconciliation. Many of the American people will not agree there is a crisis. Reconciliation must be preceded by a commitment of some sort by divergent interests that they will at least combine their enthusiasm, talents, and public posture on one point. They must combine in recognizing that we have an energy crisis.

I think if we started the reconciliation by agreeing on that, we would begin to find some areas we could move in. If we do not at least approach this point, the solution is going to come about without reconciliation, through some kind of confrontation, with drastic economic and social problems as the result.

Truth in this case, as in most, is far more than statistics, since statistics can be manipulated to support almost any proposition. The reliance of this nation on energy for every pursuit of life means to me that, if we do not know the full truth of our desperate situation, the nation will be the loser—not just the poor, or the commuter, or the user of propane, or the oil industry. This is a basic truth that so far has apparently escaped realization by a majority of our citizens and their leaders.

This truth having failed to be generally realized, politicians have had trouble identifying the national interest, and have been unwilling to take the risks necessary to develop a national energy policy that in any conceivable form must be disadvantageous to some major interest. But the fact is that, for a variety of reasons (and there is enough fault to go around), this nation is an energy-importing nation. At this point in our history, nearly two years after the Arab oil embargo almost brought us to our knees, we are still arguing about whether we actually have an energy problem and, if so, who we ought to blame.

We must convince the American people that our situation is extremely critical, and that even if all the suspicions and accusations against the oil industry were true, and that even if all those faults could be corrected overnight by some miracle, tomorrow we would still have the energy dilemma we have today. We would still be importing more than one-third of the oil we use. Moreover, every day the proportion of oil we must import would be increasing, so that our destiny would not be ours to shape. Our destiny would be—will be—to hope that foreign oil prices do not go so high that they destroy our economic vitality and that foreign producers do not cut off that one-third of our supply for any reason they care to choose. This is the dark truth the American people ought to know and the politicians ought to be telling them, promoting recognition of a genuine national problem, the magnitude and consequence of which dwarfs lesser concerns including regional and consumer interests.

We are not engaged in an academic undertaking here. Nothing that has been done on the principal issue in our country—from the day of the embargo till today—has been done from the view that the only way to arrive at reconciliation between interests that are real and apparently divergent is for there to be a desire to solve the problem. Anyone's definition of reconciliation must involve that. We must discuss the question whether there is a crisis and we have done that, and then we ought to discuss whether there are ways we can get across to the American people the fact that—for all our differences, for all our insinuations, for all the accusations of obscene profits, unethical conduct, and the like, and for all the self-serving cliches about supply, demand, free enterprise, and the like—we can at least agree on the starting premise. There is no viable approach to reconciliation unless there is an honest effort made in that direction.

I would like to emphasize one dimension of the crisis. I have been on the budget committee since it was formed in the Congress, and it appears to me there are two problems in our country that are so serious they deserve a different kind of attention from that given our ordinary problems. One is the problem of the American economy and what we ought to do to resolve it, and the other is the energy crisis and what we ought to do to resolve it. And one of the reasons the energy problem is so difficult to deal with, in addition to the lack of recognition that the problem exists, is the current economic dilemma. Citizens are understandably frightened by the instability of an economy characterized by economic recession, high unemployment and continuing inflation.

It is in our national interest to address the major problems of economy and energy simultaneously. In fact, to find a remedy for one without relation to the other is to have found no remedy at all, even though either problem taken by itself presents challenge enough. It is immediately apparent that many of the remedies that would help to stabilize our nation's economy are in direct conflict with steps designed to lead to energy independence, or even to lower dependence on foreign sources. And therein lies the greatest problem in trying to reconcile consumer and producer interests—consumer interests run parallel to stabilizing the national economy while producer interests are advanced by our becoming more energy-independent. Consequently, both of these interests can be (and have been) equated with the true and overriding national interest. Unfortunately, the failure to recognize that both are equally important and interdependent has led to an air of confrontation between the opposing sides, with the parties on each side claiming their side has staked out an exclusive hold on the national interest.

These problems of energy and the economy are intertwined and they are of serious and significant proportions. Not only must we decide that there is indeed a crisis, but when we agree on that we must also admit how serious that crisis is. We must look at the give-and-take that will be required in this reconciliation from the standpoint that this is a truly national crisis, equatable in our history only with a major war. The crisis must be talked about in terms of the survival of this nation and some of its basic institutions—of its economic well-being and its standard of living. If it is looked at from that vantage point, there will be new room for reconciliation.

In looking at reconciliation from that standpoint, what we are trying to reconcile and the roots of the reconciliation effort take on a new dimension, according to the way the reconciling parties proceed and what will happen if they do not proceed. A simple analogy would be a husband and wife trying to reconcile: obviously there are important things that hang in the balance, and it is not at all the same thing as reconciling two young children who have had a fight. There must be a lot more give-and-take with the husband and wife because the final product is a more serious one.

To me, the response of this nation ought to be similar to the response to an all-out war. There is just as much at stake, in my opinion, for unless we solve our energy problems, we risk the destruction of our way of life on a scale usually only attributable to losing a war. That, to me, is a possible consequence of the lack of a national energy policy. We must have a policy that treats the various interests as fairly as possible, but subordinates them to the main interest—the survival of the essentials of the American way of life with all its manifold blessings.

I should point out here that there are a number of things that contribute to our inability to arrive at basic agreement on the fact that we have a crisis. One of these is the institution called Congress. There is no doubt about it that to bring about reconciliation, Congress itself will have to become more unified in its approach to the energy crisis. Institutionally, Congress must rid itself of the diversity of committees that handle the problem and must understand it as an American problem and speak with one voice, one set of questions, not bombarding the American people from all sides. I do not know whether this can occur, but I think it is more apt to occur if we would agree on the first premise, that there is a crisis, because if the Congress did believe that, its members might move in the direction of changing their institutional approaches.

Those interests outside of Congress that have joined themselves together, apparently on opposite sides of the arena, could treat the problem in one of two ways. If they hold fast, if they insist on irrational solutions, if they insist they cannot give and take in the process, reconciliation becomes impossible. As one who has talked with both sides, it seems to me that the producer is willing to concede that this is not a typical free enterprise problem, because of the cartel, because of our dependence on it, because of many things we have done in the oil and gas and energy field in the past. I think there is some room for play here, some room for give-and-take. But I think the producers dig in when there appears to be a constant bombardment from the other side to the effect that there is only one solution and that the producers cannot be part of it because they are themselves the problem.

Convincing our leaders of the problem of the economy is far less difficult than convincing them of the problem of our energy situation, but we must find a mechanism for doing it. Perhaps we are further along than I have indicated, but the next thirty days or so, during which the Congress and the President have another chance to work out a compromise plan, will tell that story. Critical to the success of that venture will be congressional recognition that unrestricted promotion of producer interests can sabotage economic stability and that unrestricted promotion of consumer interests would only worsen our energy problems.

The art of politics is an art of reconciliation and compromise. All of us must be prepared to accept some trade-offs because, as Charles Schultze said in testimony before the Senate Budget Committee, "it is literally impossible to define an ideal energy policy. . . . [It] is important, therefore . . . to seek a set of compromises which minimizes the damage to some goals as we try to attain others."

That kind of compromise encompassing both consumer and producer interests, doing the least possible damage to either, is what must occur if we are to resolve these dilemmas. Eternal confrontation will eventually spell disaster for all our people, whether consumers or producers. I apologize if I have become overly dramatic, but I believe we must generate concern in people across this land, and through them, in their representatives in Congress, because I believe that given the nature of the political arena, their lack of concern cannot be allowed to continue.

I hope I have established my view that any particular interest, including those competing with each other, can be subordinated to the national interest when that interest is clearly and generally recognized. The answer to the issue of political reconciliation of competing regional interests relating to energy is in principle not difficult at all—to promote either at the expense of the national interest would be irresponsible. On the other hand, to use the overriding national interest as a reason to promote one of the interests over the other would likewise be irresponsible.

Let me conclude by saying that, contrary to what some might think because I come from a state with large production, I am firmly convinced that reconciliation must occur. I am firmly convinced that the American people would accept the reconciliation and the terms of the reconciliation if they were given the truth.

50

COMMENTARY

Jim Langdon

I commend Senator Domenici for his statement. I agree that a lack of reconciliation would be disastrous for the nation, and would deny us the opportunity to solve our problems. We must forget our recriminations, forget the battle we had on the Machiasport refinery, and seek solutions to the nation's energy problem. There are solutions.

One point keeps occurring to me. When we think about the oil-producing states, we are generally thinking about the three or four largest ones—Texas, Louisiana, Oklahoma, and New Mexico—as though they were the only places we could expect to find new reserves. The people of New England and Massachusetts think in terms of their distance from these sources. They are at the end of the supply lines, and this does increase the cost of their gas when it finally arrives. However, there are some alternatives available.

I doubt anyone here has any misconceptions on where I stand on deregulation: I am certainly for it. Deregulation would open up a vast new area of supply for the nation. In West Virginia and in Ohio, there are good prospects for natural gas, but they are in areas that cannot be drilled for 51 cents. These areas presumably have an intrastate market, and the question may therefore be asked, Why are they not drilling, if no one is going to tell them the price they will receive for their gas? But, as a matter of fact, Federal Power Commission pricing does control the drilling activity in states like West Virginia and Ohio because they do not have a significant intrastate mechanism for marketing natural gas. As long as they do not have that mechanism, all the gas they produce will go into an interstate pipeline at FPC-controlled prices.

Perhaps it would be worthwhile to look at the case of New Mexico. New Mexico has no intrastate marketing system. Its industry and its people are served with gas produced in New Mexico but carried through an interstate pipeline. The same situation holds true, to a large extent, for the state of Oklahoma. It is true even in a state like Louisiana. I think Commissioner Ray Sutton of the Louisiana Corporation Commission, who is here, would agree that his state, and others, really need to expand their intrastate marketing mechanisms to encourage production of natural gas.

It has been said that drilling activity does not respond to high prices, and indeed that 75 or 80 cents may be about as high as could be expected to get any

51

additional natural gas. This has simply proven not to be the case in Texas. Texas has a large and complex intrastate marketing system and, consequently, a large portion of its natural gas is free from FPC pricing. Texans in fact are paying a great deal more for the natural gas they consume than is being paid for the same gas in Massachusetts and other areas on the long interstate lines.

About eighteen months ago, Lo-Vaca Gas pipeline system had a 50 percent gas shortfall: this pipeline could not meet its customer demand. This was a serious shortfall, as serious as any confronting any state in the union. The system was ordered to augment its supply of gas and was authorized to pass along the higher cost of this gas to the consumer. This resulted in some higher prices—higher costs—to the consumers, and of course they do not like to pay higher prices for home heating any more than the people in the North do. But they paid, and they do have gas. And I can tell you, it is better to have gas at a higher price than not to have any at all at a very low price. It does not make sense to set the price so low that consumers cannot get gas.

Decontrol would be one of the solutions we could look to for enhancing our supply of gas. The problem is really one of supply. I think distribution will take care of itself. I think the drilling programs will take care of themselves when there are no restrictions, whether by the Federal Power Commission or by anyone else. There is more demand for natural gas than we can meet under current pricing mechanisms.

Jim Bishop

I think it is remarkable that this regional energy issue has not blown up before. This has always been a country of competing interests. There has in fact rarely been a time when various regions were not at each others' throats over commodities and policies. Energy is one commodity that separates men from the cave, and we are all learning that it brings out everyone's worst instincts, most notably greed, as we see the consumer interests beginning to try to countervail the pressure from the producing interests whom they consider to have had the upper hand for all these years. Dealing with this separation of interests is far more difficult, I think, than dealing with OPEC. OPEC has managed to develop an orchestrated policy. The OPEC nations have many more things in common inside the cartel, it seems, than we have been able to recognize here.

One overriding point here is that this country is woefully ignorant about its own energy flows. The average consumer somehow or other has gone through school and into life without realizing precisely where energy comes from. No one has told him—not the corporations, not the press, not the politicians. It is my feeling that if more information were available, if the tremendous New England energy dependency on other regions were fully known, the people themselves might begin to take some action and the solution would, in fact, be a regional series of solutions rather than an overriding national solution. I do not myself see a national solution, because I see that the congressional debate this summer has brought out an enormous number of conflicts and special interests colliding to create the present impasse.

One thing that must be decided very quickly is this question of cheap energy. Are we going to get cheap energy back again when the cartel breaks, or is cheap energy gone forever? The debate on this question really has yet to be joined. Before this debate, before this problem can be resolved, the structure of the oil industry itself as an issue must also be resolved. It is argued in the Congress that when the producing interests did have the upper hand in this country, they created a situation that brought us where we are today. I am not sure that reconciliation is possible until the question of the structure of the industry is resolved once and for all. Who is actually going to do the work of bringing us our hydrocarbons?

DISCUSSION

GOVERNOR BOREN: I think one of the things we must consider when we talk about reconciliation is the time factor. Every day that we go on without a solution makes reconciliation more difficult. Every winter in which we have unemployment resulting from stoppages or curtailment makes reconciliation more difficult. And one of the things that concerns me about the Vice President's remarks and other remarks I have heard is that I do not know how long we can afford to go without tackling the problem for the short term, and still have any opening left for reconciliation. If we have two or three bad winters with high unemployment, we will have a situation that will make it very difficult for producing and consuming states to talk to one another. We may see the problem being resolved through force in an hysterical atmosphere, rather than through reasoned approaches. I think we must be thinking about the short-term solution while working on the long term.

Now, when I say short term, I do not only mean 180 days, though I support that proposal strongly, and by the way, I can tell you it works. We had a delegation from North Carolina, their governor and their textile and glass manufacturers, who sat down with our producers, our pipeline managers, our utilities. The prices they were negotiating were slightly less than our prevailing intrastate prices, and if they receive assurances from the government that they can have the 180 days without worrying about permanent entanglement in the interstate market, they are ready to work out a solution for this winter. I think we can do it.

Nevertheless, when we talk about the short term, we must at least be talking about keeping things together in the next four or five years, while we tackle the long-range problems of solar energy, nuclear energy, shale, shale gas, shale oil. These sources of energy are not going to be brought on-stream in the next two to three years, no matter how quickly we work. And since the things the Vice President talked about are not going to happen within a year or two or three, the question is, what is going to hold us together in a mood in which we can reconcile our differences in the meantime?

When we talk about this four-to-five-year short run, we are talking about oil and gas that can be fed into delivery systems that are here right now. To be sure, there are delivery systems that are going to be built in West Virginia or Ohio or New Mexico in the future—five years from now, ten years from now. But the question is, what can we do to increase the supplies of natural gas and oil in the areas that need it desperately, while we look for long-range regional solutions and for other investment?

SENATOR DOMENICI: I would like to ask Judge Langdon a question. How do we treat the problem that arises because the normal supply/demand equation has been suppressed for a number of years, and we will now have a shortage for a number of years? How do we say that for some, natural gas will cost two or three or four times what it would otherwise be worth, even with the added costs of new fields or the like, because we have not had a typical American free-enterprise supply/demand equation?

JUDGE LANGDON: I think that if we were to remove controls, the supplies would become available. Governor Boren has told me that in the state of Oklahoma, they have perhaps 200 billion cubic feet of gas per day that might be available for the interstate market on a short-term basis. This is not surplus gas. It is simply gas they do not need for the present short term. In Texas we have in the neighborhood of 500 million cubic feet of gas per day that would probably be available for the short term. This could help out, and it ought to be made available to other states, but of course the producers do not want to become tied to an interstate pipeline and have their gas contaminated. As Chairman Nassikas knows, once we get the gas in the interstate pipeline, it will be trapped, and the intrastate producer does not want to get trapped in that position.

SENATOR DOMENICI: The state of Louisiana would say there is a short-term excess in its intrastate line of 256 million cubic feet per day. Texas is estimated to have between 500 million and one billion cubic feet per day excess. If all this were made available, it would take care of about two-thirds of the projected short-fall, even if we had a severe winter. Now what is the price going to be under those circumstances?

JUDGE LANGDON: I frankly do not know what the price would be. I think it would be a negotiated price and would be substantially what our Texas people are paying for new gas right now. We are not asking anyone in other states to do anything we are not doing ourselves. There are a number of restraints that would prevent the producers from gouging the public: there are more statesmen among the producers than many would think. The producers have been depicted as criminals and vicious people. As a matter of fact, the way some of the legislation is designed in House bill 9464, some of the repeal provisions are far more severe than those we have to control the Mafia in this country.

MR. NASSIKAS: In answer to your question, Senator Domenici, what the price will be is not capable of being precisely measured. The estimates depend on which economists are giving the estimates. As a lawyer with some experience in this field, and not as an economist, I would suggest that, on the basis of Federal Power Commission studies on intrastate price levels, the price would range from somewhere in the area of a dollar up to three dollars, which is a 200 percent range.

On average, as we computed it for July 1975, the intrastate price level for jurisdictional gas companies selling in the intrastate market, was $1.26/Mcf or a million Btus. I think that is low because it only includes jurisdictional companies, and the weighting of it does not include sales by non-jurisdictional companies, which we know are in the range of $1.50 to $2.25.

We also have a rule recently issued by the Federal Power Commission, and an order on that rule, to allow industries to purchase gas directly from producers. They can then have that gas transported in pipeline systems with a load factor—as a result of curtailment—that can accommodate the additional load.

I think, on the basis of that rule, some industries may be paying as high as $3.00/ or even $4.00/Mcf. And because I think this is the kind of discussion that ought to be candid and open, I will not suggest that the price is going to hover around $1.25: it is going to go up as high as $3.00 to $5.00 in the spot market. On average, the price levels I would predict with fair confidence may not exceed $1.50 per million Btus.

We have spoken of surplus gas. Surplus gas—let us say 500 to 750 billion cubic feet—is trying to find a market apart from the intrastate market. This is gas that is simply available to be produced—gas that is available immediately, over the short range in the next thirty days to six months. Now in priority two—the large industrial users of gas that do not have an alternate fuel except propane, which may be in short supply (users such as the glass industry, some parts of the textile industry, some parts of the steel industry)—that 500 billion cubic feet of gas would prevent unemployment this coming winter. These users are scattered from South Carolina through the middle Atlantic states, and in Ohio, up to Pennsylvania and southern New York.

Even though this is a small amount of gas overall, when we are speaking of 22 trillion cubic feet nationally, for our immediate purposes this is an enormous block of gas that could really salvage part of our economy in winter 1975–1976. The winter shortfall would be the equivalent of about 5,400,000 barrels of oil.

CHARLES DiBONA, executive vice president, American Petroleum Institute: I think Chairman Nassikas is correct, and I would go further and say that the point he makes is relevant to the question what the eventual price might be. There are among the remaining users a substantial number who can convert to other fuels. The other fuels will not run over $2.00 a thousand cubic feet, so that for many users the alternative will be to take $2.00-a-thousand-cubic-feet gas, or to take these other cheaper fuels. The exercise of this alternative should significantly reduce the total amount of the shortfall. Very large increases in the shortfall are highly unlikely.

What we have instead is a moderate sales crisis for the natural gas that will be bought by those who do not shift to other fuels. This crisis will principally occur among those who have no alternative and who, if this temporary supply were not made available, would find themselves importing gas or importing fuels at $4.00 and $5.00 a thousand cubic feet. From the standpoint of the nation's interest, making this gas available is clearly a preferred alternative, and from the standpoint of the consumer, prices are unlikely to go over the suggested $2.00 levels.

MR. MURPHY: I would like to join Chairman Nassikas and Mr. DiBona but take their point further. If I seem to be a fundamentalist in economic view, I guess it is because I am. I think we ought to remind ourselves of a homely saying that Professor Pigou used to give his students, and it was simply this: "Prices have work to do." We heard the Vice President, and putting aside for a moment the question of whether energy development is to be done by government or private enterprise, we know it cannot be done in the next four or five years in any case. The only way this nation is going to get the Btus that it needs now is to reinvent the coal industry. This is very unimaginative.

But just yesterday, when I was going through our saw mill in Western Arkansas with the manager, I saw the fuel oil standby tanks. I asked, "Well, have you been served notice of interruption yet?" He said, "No, no. We think we are going to make it till January, and we will probably have only two or three weeks of interruption then." So I said, "Have you thought of switching your plant entirely to Oklahoma coal?" I would have thought I had mentioned holy water to the devil. "No, I am not going to use coal," he answered.

Now he is getting gas, which is a premium fuel, at a discount. He is not stupid, and he is going to continue to use that premium fuel as long as he can get it at a discount, and it is only when he is priced out of the market that he will switch to coal. He has to be made to switch. He is not going to shut his plant down; there is not going to be unemployment there. But when the gas gets out of his reach—and he is in a tough thin-margin business—then he will have to switch to Oklahoma coal, and he will do it. The price of his fuel will be somewhat higher than it is now, but the higher price is something he can absorb. He is going to have to absorb it. Multiply that homely example by thousands and we can see, I believe, how we can have rational energy use in this country, over the next four or five years, while we are waiting for the exotics.

We should let the fuels compete with each other. The resources must be allocated one way or another, and if we do not let the impartial market perform the allocation, it must be performed some other way. Then there will be distortions and inequities.

58

MR. PEABODY: Coming from Massachusetts and having been governor once, I do not want to give the impression that this conference is getting two governors for the price of one: I want to speak not as the former governor of Massachusetts but as the head of a national organization, Americans for Energy Independence, and I want to speak for the people who are hoping to use this energy that is in such short supply.

We have been talking about one region's being pitted against another, but it is clear at least to us at this table that we are short of energy in every region, and that even if we put to work all the energy sources that we have available currently—whether coal or gas or nuclear or oil—and even if we conserve, we are still going to have to import foreign oil. There are problems that we must face in the next five or six years in getting this energy on line—we have been discussing at some length the gas and oil problems, and they are important, but some of the others are as deeply important.

For example, we have not produced a pound more coal in the last two years than we produced before the energy shortage started, and yet our aim is to double our production of coal in the next ten years. Why have we not increased our production? The coal industry will say it is because there is no understanding of coal industry problems in the Congress. Congress will say there is no understanding of the nation's problems in the coal industry. But in fact, coal has been left out as a step-brother, and no one is really saying how we are going to get it—whether it be by surface mining with all the environmental problems that must be solved, or whether it be by deepmining with air sulfur dioxide problems that are involved. Yet we must make some national decisions here. It is the consumers who are going to be up against it if we do not make these decisions soon, and I was happy to hear Vice President Rockefeller say that this energy corporation would have other purposes than merely to lend money—that it was designed to try to bring together those who had problems with all of these agencies to help resolve the problems. One of these problems is in coal, and of course some of the problems are nuclear, too. But even if we go all out in every area, we are still going to have to import oil.

DONALD CRAVEN, Federal Energy Administration: I would just like to emphasize what Mr. Murphy has said and what I think is really a key to the problem—that until we let the price of premium fuels such as natural gas reflect their true value to society, we are not going to burn our abundant resources such as coal. We are going to continue to burn gas inefficiently in utility boilers. We are not going to bring reason into the debate on the Clean Air Act that is now going on in Congress.

Coal, as you know, is demand-limited. It is limited by restrictive environmental regulations. Until the price of alternate fuels does reflect their true value, coal is not going to be a desirable fuel in this country. I think this really is the key to the utilization of coal and to the utilization of nuclear energy. I understand that the

California Bar Association just recently endorsed the nuclear initiative in the state of California. California does not want to drill offshore. The citizens of California do not want to use nuclear energy. As long as natural gas is available cheaply, opposition to offshore drilling and opposition to nuclear energy will continue to exist. Before we can use our abundant resources like coal and nuclear energy, we simply must decide what we will be willing to pay for oil and natural gas.

GWEN MURPHREE, League of Women Voters: It has been my experience in the League of Women Voters that politicians generally respond to their constituency as they should. That is, after all, their job. I have also found that politicians quite frequently can be statesmanlike and take the lead in seeking solutions to problems, and certainly if we are going to have reconciliation, it behooves the politicians to go out on the limb and seek solutions. However, I think the politicians ought to be reassured that if they go out on the limb, it will not be sawed off behind them, and therein lies the problem that Mr. Bishop posed when he asked what the people of this country know and understand about the energy problem.

Politics is people, and until the people have the information they need, they will not arrive at a consensus on what is needed and what is wanted. One of the difficulties with regionalism is that people do not understand the energy flow: they do not know where they get their energy, or how much they get from any one source; they do not even know how much they can consume. Last year, the League of Women Voters held a series of conferences, and we had the people who came from the various states prepare profiles of their states. It became evident—and it was surprising—to many of those people that they were totally dependent on energy from somewhere else. I think it was surprising to the Texas people to find out that Texas will be an energy-consuming state, an energy-importing state, by 1985. The well does eventually run dry. The point is that the people need to know where their energy comes from, that all of us are in this together. It is not one section of the country against the other. The press, the media, organizations like the League of Women Voters, have a responsibility to provide the needed information. The point that energy is no longer going to be cheap—I do not care what kind of energy we use, it will cost more money—has not been made loudly or clearly by any politician at any level in this government. I would also like to suggest that if we wait for the Congress to reorganize itself and have fewer committees than it has considering the energy problem, the problem will either go away or we will all be done in.

GOVERNOR BOREN: One of the things that puzzles me is that on a particular phase of natural gas deregulation we have been able to get thirty-one governors from various regions of the country to see that deregulation might be in the national interest, but we cannot get the members of Congress to see that compromises and trade-offs must be made to get us off dead center. Since we are talking about reconciliation, one of the things that would be useful here would be to try to determine what are the irreducible minimum points we can agree upon, from whatever region or background we come.

One of the points, it seems to me (though I did not quite hear the Vice President say this), is that we all realize energy is going to be expensive, whatever form of energy it is. The days of cheap energy are over. I think we also realize that it will take massive capital investment in order to gain the kind of energy supplies this country needs, whether we are talking about existing conventional sources or new kinds of energy. I repeat, we are talking about an immense capital investment, and whether we come from New England or California or Oklahoma or Michigan, we must realize this.

This investment must come from somewhere. We are talking about increasing the percentage of our gross national product that goes into capital investment. This means, to be honest, that we must reduce the percentage of gross national product going somewhere else, and that what we reduce somewhere else, we must channel into capital investment. The question I wanted to ask Vice President Rockefeller was, where are we going to cut? What part of our current use of our gross national product are we going to give up? I have my own beliefs. I think transfer payments by government would be a good place to start.

Let me ask, can we all agree that the development of new sources of energy, whether the energy is coal or nuclear or traditional or solar, will take a great amount of capital investment, either by government or by private sources? And can we agree that it will take some sacrifice in channeling a certain percentage of our gross national product into capital investment, taking it from somewhere else?

MR. UDALL: Governor Boren has sketched in some important parts of the big picture. I want to make some general comments about what has been said here and about the whole theme of the conference, because I believe it is important to recognize that the regional hostility developing in this country is related in some instances to environmental arguments, in some instances to economic arguments, and in some instances to both.

The bumper sticker I saw in Alaska, "Sierra, go home," is the pro-pipeline people putting down the people who had questions about the pipeline. The bumper sticker in New Mexico that says, "Texan, go home," is an environmental bumper sticker. In fact, the citizens of New Mexico would just as soon, some of them, that most of us did not go there and settle, and I do not blame them for that. The Texas bumper sticker, "Let the bastards freeze in the dark," is, I suppose, directed at New England. This is the kind of thing that is going on, and we must recognize that it is going on.

The attitudes developing in the Rocky Mountain states have come swiftly through Colorado, Wyoming, and Montana: they have not as yet reached Utah. These attitudes are pitting producer states against consumer states. But we recognize that the great strength of this country, large as it is, has been the federal idea. Because of that federal idea we have treated our resources as a national resource.

I am old enough to have seen natural gas being flared in Texas, and flaring natural gas was an enormous waste of a resource. The United States pioneered the steps to end the waste: we built huge pipeline systems, and made natural gas into a national resource, where it had been wasted before. That was a great thing. Indeed, in the last thirty years it is probably the most important thing we have done for energy.

I will save my conservation speech for tomorrow, but I am dismayed that I find no hint of considering the next few years in Vice President Rockefeller's presentation today. I am not dismayed that some of the big coal plants or nuclear power plants that were planned a year ago are not being built. I think we do not need them because high prices and other factors are forcing us to use less electric power than we have been using in some regions of the country. I do not see anything we can do in the short term except to conserve. Even so, a year ago, the American Enterprise Institute held a seminar—I was not here—and Secretary Laird came out with a conclusion that we probably were going to have to go to gas rationing. But no one wants to talk about that conclusion.

I would like to suggest that the free market works very well in a climate of abundance. Of course, we had an abundance of petroleum in the 1960s but we also had the oil import program that I administered which was an aberration. It was designed to protect the economy of this country; indeed we used to talk about it in terms of national security. I think it did protect the economy, and that was the most important thing, but I had mixed feelings about the program then, and I have now. On the other hand, when we are on the edge of shortages—and that is where Chairman Nassikas and Judge Langdon and others have said we are now, particularly with natural gas—we must recognize that the free-market idea breaks down in dealing with shortages. In my view, the way you share shortages is to cut back consumption, to ration, to conserve.

I think it important that we not confuse the economic arguments and the environmental arguments, and that we realize they overlap. If we reach the point where regional hostility prevents the country from doing what we should rationally and logically do as a single people, then we are in real trouble. Our resiliency as a nation, our ability to submerge regional interest or selfish interest in the national interest, is being tested. We must have, I am afraid, a kind of leadership we are not getting either from the Congress or the executive to do something about it.

MR. CAHN: First, I would like to say a kind word for politicians and the media. Mr. Murphy says that the people around the country do not really believe that whatever energy we have in the future is going to cost more than energy has cost in the past. Now I have heard a number of politicians, including the President of the United States, say it will cost more. I have read a couple of excellent pieces in

Newsweek magazine—whether they were written by Mr. Bishop I do not know, but they went to that point—and certainly, the *Wall Street Journal* has repeatedly said that energy will cost more than it has. Perhaps the question is whether anyone is listening.

Second, Secretary Udall made a statement that I do not agree with: he said that the free-market system works in time of affluence and plenty, but does not work in times of scarcity. I think it is less apt to work efficiently in times of affluence and great supplies, because then there is lots of room for waste. But it works best and quickest and most efficiently in time of scarcity.

MR. MILLER: Coming from a rural state and having spoken with colleagues across the northern tier of the United States (with the possible exception of the state of Washington), I can say what most concerns all of us is a question of allocation for the short term until we can work out our problems in the long term. If a timetable were worked out and it were agreed upon that by a set time we would have to make our choice, I think the people would face up to it—but they will not face up to it when they are dealing with something they do not really understand, when they are not given any idea what the future is going to bring. We see this with the major oil companies, in the conditions for renewal leases; they will not guarantee a source of supply. And we can see only further problems coming when this new element enters into negotiations. At the end of the pipeline, it is not only a question of getting new refineries, but also a question of a source of supply.

The second thing, which I think Jim Bishop hit on, is the feeling that comes from dealing with monopoly industries, the feeling the householder has because he must get his electricity from the company to which his house is connected. I think the oil industry will have to come to grips with the fact that, no matter what solution we come up with in oil and natural gas, there is going to be extraordinary public distrust if the solution is administered in the same way as solutions appear to have been administered in the past. I am not saying whether the appearance is true. But I have been a trial lawyer, and I guarantee that the worst kind of defendant any trial lawyer can have is a public utility, because everyone has to live with the utilities and everyone dislikes them. And the reason people dislike them is that, once they move in, they have no choice as to which utility they have to live with.

I believe that the oil companies will have to come to grips with the fact that they are not popular; they will have to recognize that no matter whether they should be the scapegoat, they will be, and they may not be able to take what they consider their fair share in the marketplace. I can see that they want to go slowly because they are afraid of what the real ramifications of their moves could be. But there will have to be some giving on their part as a first step.

MR. UNSELL: I want to say that Mr. Murphy and I finally agree on something. He is an economic fundamentalist and so am I. But I think we must sometimes look at these things in an historical perspective, and one of the best examples of the working of the free-market mechanism came after World War II. As we all know, during World War II everything was controlled—not just oil, but everything. I remember the IPAA went through innumerable hearings during World War II, and finally published a little pamphlet called *Four Years and Forty Hearings*—four years of trying to get crude oil above a dollar a barrel.

As Judge Langdon knows only too well, we were producing not at capacity but above capacity. We were gutting fields all over Texas to conclude that war effort. And we had a genuine oil shortage in 1945, when the economy started converting back to peacetime ways. Harry Truman had the good sense to deregulate everything, and the industry responded to deregulation by going out and achieving an uninterrupted increase of 136 percent in drilling, right up to 1957. We not only got rid of the shortages, we had 2.8 million barrels a day of crude oil shut in the ground for want of a market in 1957. This was the market working in a shortage situation.

The judge brought up another point I would like to comment on, that the politicians seem to say "When the industry was in charge, it did not do the job." I do not think the government can get off the hook that easily. I remember the first oil crisis we had in 1957. There were different faces, but Senator O'Mahoney had a hearing and the dome almost came off of the Capitol. One of the things the Senate was shocked about in those days was a story that ARAMCO told about the United States government. King Ibn Saud became aroused because he found out that our government was taxing more out of ARAMCO than he was making. We sent a mission over there from our government to teach him how to tax the industry and keep him pacified so that our private enterprise could go ahead and develop Middle East oil. In other words, our government spent years attracting our private entrepreneurs in this country to find oil elsewhere.

I know Mr. Udall was accused, rightly or wrongly, of causing an exodus of refining capacity from this country when he was administering—or, as some said, maladministering—the oil import program. I would like to observe that, in addition to some of the things the government did to encourage our private companies to go abroad, it clamped price controls on crude oil and natural gas at home. And, from the surplus in 1957, when we drilled 58,000 wells, we went steadily downhill for sixteen years. We drilled 27,000 wells in 1973, less than half as many as in 1957. Now the market is working again. In 1974, we increased drilling in this country 23 percent, by some 5,000 wells. In 1975 we are going to go to 37,000. That is a 10,000-well increase in two years. No one can tell me the market is not working. I am not saying this will solve our problem, but I say that, if we get the government off of the back of the private entrepreneurs in this industry, that will go a long way toward solving some of our problems.

Mr. Murphy mentioned that the industry generally and the IPAA specifically have endorsed Mr. Ford's thirty-nine-month phase-out. I do not know of an instance in the history of man when a government ever solved a shortage of anything by price regimentation: I do not think it has ever been done. I think that a thirty-nine-month phase-out is a rather long phase-out if we consider the fact that Congress has abandoned price controls on everything else. We had shortages of chickens, beef, wheat, and corn about three years back because of Phase III, and the result was that we got rid of Phase III.

I think the industry is more than willing to go along with phased deregulation. Vermont Royster's newspaper had an editorial I thought had one telling item in it. On the very day that gasoline was selling for 38 cents wholesale in New York, it was selling for 38 cents wholesale in Rotterdam. And there is not one $5.00 barrel of oil in the market in Rotterdam—all the oil is $13.00. I do not think that a phased decontrol of crude oil prices in this country or the new gas deregulation that the Senate has voted on would cause an economic collapse of the United States. On the other hand, I have just received the Chase Bank's analysis of the thirty largest oil companies. One of the things in this report I think should disturb us is the fact that the crude oil supply of these thirty companies in the free world declined 1 billion 157 million barrels last year, and that 942 million—almost 90 percent of that—was in the Western Hemisphere. The Federal Energy Administration's latest figures show that these companies got 59 million barrels less from Canada and 417 million barrels less from Venezuela in 1974 than they did in the previous year. The unmet demand has been transferred to the Middle East so that we are now 50 percent more dependent on the Middle East for crude oil than we were at the onset of the embargo two years ago. I could not help relating this fact to the Kuwaiti finance minister's speech at the National Press Club three weeks ago last Friday in which he said, "Yes, the Arab nations are going to continue to use the embargo as a weapon against the West." And he used the word "weapon." When we talk about the cost of deregulation, I have to relate that to the cost of 50 or 60 percent dependence on Middle East oil, the cost of being a permanent hostage of that kind of threat as a way of life. What would be the cost of that?

GOVERNOR BOREN: We know that we must have an adequate price if there is to be drilling and exploration: that is one of the things we do know, whether we are talking about oil and gas, whether we are talking about development of coal, or whatever. Before there will be investment, there must be a price that will at least return what is put into the investment and, one hopes, a little bit more. But at least the investment must not be a losing proposition. This is one of the things that discourages me about the Stevenson-Hollings bill. It actually says "You will produce at $1.30" and it makes it mandatory for you to do so. On natural gas, for example, if you drill a well and find out it costs you $2.00 to produce, it still becomes an illegal act for you not to continue to produce something that is in fact causing you an absolute loss.

With coal there are environmental problems that are slowing production down. With nuclear energy there are environmental problems that are slowing production down. Something will have to hold us together for the next two or three years while we talk about the long-range solution, whether it is nuclear energy, or coal, or solar energy, or whatever. And we know we must have a price that is adequate to attract investment—not only that, but the investor must have the money in his pocket to invest it.

How do we create an atmosphere in this country that will allow increases in the price of oil and gas—I think this is particularly important as far as exploration for new gas is concerned—to the point where exploration and development are an attractive investment? How do we get the money into the people's pockets to make that investment? As I mentioned before, I think this involves some shifts in GNP. How do we do these things and at the same time assure the governor or senator or representative from New England who reflects the fears of his people— fears that look back at the history of the oil and gas industry—that the prices will not rise so fast that New England will be eaten up with inflation? How do we assure them, for example, that the specific items they cannot do without—fuel oil or propane—will not have to bear an impact they cannot bear? Of course there are some things we can conserve: we can conserve gasoline a lot more easily than we can conserve home fuel oil.

These seem to me to be the kinds of questions we must start asking. How do we get prices up enough to cause people to want to invest their money? How do we get the money in their pockets to invest? And then, at the same time, how do we give some kind of assurance to consuming states that they will not be hit hard on items like home fuel oil? How do we assure them the average price will not rise so quickly that it will eat them up with inflation?

Let us suppose that we have phased decontrol of oil and decontrol of new natural gas, through some mechanism that would try to prevent the average price from going up too rapidly. Let us suppose that long-term contracts would prevent too rapid a rise in the price of natural gas. We still must answer the questions, how do we solve New England's problem with home fuel oil, and how do we solve New England's problem with propane? How do we solve these two specific problems of expensive commodities in short supply?

MR. UNSELL: I should mention that we have just filed a statement with Mr. Dingell's committee in which we endorsed stand-by price and allocation controls for propane for the federal government. As far as New England fuel oil is concerned, on residual fuel they are 99 percent dependent on foreign oil, and the domestic industry of course does not even influence that, much less control it. I think the market will take care of the home heating fuel situation.

MARLOW W. COOK, National Energy Project Advisory Council: I think Governor Boren laid out the model for getting out of this situation—a proper economic incentive for industry to go out and get these badly needed commodities. Everyone is searching for a magic number that will provide the incentive. I can say on behalf of the consuming states that it is more important for them that the number be high enough to get the job done than it is for the oil industry. Most of the independents phased out in the 1950s anyway because at that time the price for oil and gas would not permit them to stay in business. I am saying now that no one can pick the magic number. It is too fleeting—inflation, the cost of doing business, as well as all the gross national product, are too much involved in this—for someone to pick the number. But the price has to be set high enough to do the job. The oil and gas is there. We need the economic incentive to go get it.

JUDGE LANGDON: Let me draw a parallel. There is another commodity that is now in short supply, and that is yellow cake. The government, I believe, has had a fixed price of about $8.00 a pound for yellow cake. Probably we have either produced or found all the uranium we are going to find in this country at $8.00 a pound. And I believe that the current market price is moving on up in the neighborhood of $20.00 or $24.00 a pound. This means our producers are having to go a lot deeper than they used to go and they are having to operate their mines in a different way from the way they used to operate them.

By the way, I just returned from a trip. Our jurisdiction in Texas has been enlarged to include strip mining and the supervision of uranium mining. So I made a little trip down through Arkansas and Tennessee and Kentucky and Indiana about three or four weeks ago. We have environmental protection regulations that require these mining pits to be properly covered and so forth. But I was asking about some of the costs involved in meeting these standards and whether or not bonds were required by the coal operators. The operator said, "Yes, but we can't get the bonds up high enough." I asked, "Why can't you?" He said, "You know, a lot of this land that they're mining is $25.00 to $50.00 land; that's the market price for the land. Some of our standards are such that it requires anywhere from $15,000 to $25,000 per acre to restore the land." Of course the consumer is going to have to pay that price: the coal companies cannot bear it all. If the consumer will not pay the price, we will have to find a cheaper way to restore that land. However the price is paid, these things are costs of mining. I would like to respond to what Jim Bishop said a while ago, too, with regard to the question where this blame really lies. I have been involved with the regulation of oil and gas companies in Texas, now, for going on thirteen years. And oil and gas executives are not all saints down there by a long shot: we have to watch them pretty close, because they are a highly competitive people, and they operate in the same reservoirs with each other. Now, A. V. Jones, who is here, is a good independent: I think he is one who has observed the way we do watch the oil and gas industries.

I think the thing that Stewart Udall is talking about is what has brought out these signs "Let the bastards freeze in the dark." What has brought them out are the comments—like those Senator Jackson has made—about obscene profits. There is nothing obscene about profits that must be high enough to cover the cost of producing oil or gas. This is the kind of rhetoric I think we must cool. We must start talking about constructive solutions, recognizing the costs that go into this kind of discovery and production and operation.

I agree completely with Gwen Murphree that we have already passed an era of cheap oil and gas and, for that matter, the era of any cheap fuel. I do not think we are going to see our energy demands brought down materially during our lifetime. It may be when we achieve fusion or some similar technological break-through that we will have cheaper energy again, but not during the lifetime of most of us in this room. We are just not going to see any more cheap energy.

ELVIS J. STAHR, president, National Audubon Society: While I have had a lot of comments come to mind in the course of the day, someone has usually made them for me. But I do have a contribution toward constructive solutions. To bor-row Judge Langdon's term, I have a philosophical point and a practical point, a point from which some reconciliation might take off.

It may not be generally recognized that the conservation movement has been around a good long time. And most conservationists have always deplored the underpricing of our natural resources. We have always been in favor of charging the true cost, if only to avoid or to minimize waste which, to a conservationist, is about the worst conceivable thing. But when we say full cost, when we go that far with the industry, we would like to see the industry come back with us and include the full cost of the externalities and not just the direct costs of production. It hurts our feelings a little bit when much of the industry fights tooth-and-nail against a reasonable compromise strip-mining reclamation measure intended to bring the externalities into the picture. The philosophy of that legislation, which passed by large majorities in both houses of Congress two or three times, is simply the old American conservative philosophy that whoever makes a mess ought to clean it up.

My point is that we will go with the producers on full cost if they will go with us on full cost. In the process, the nation is bound to benefit because there will be a lot less waste. This is something that higher prices do achieve. There may be inequities or temporary inequities resulting, and those should be taken care of some other way than by having a false market value placed on something that is really very valuable.

MR. DiBONA: I have two brief comments. The first is a remark on something Governor Boren said about heating oil being absolutely essential and something one cannot cut back on. I just have trouble believing that anyone who lived in an Oxford college for three years could really believe that. But there are two points Governor Boren raised on which I would like to speak. On the question whether we agreed that there was a real capital need here, I note that while no one said they agreed, no one said they disagreed. I presume there is some general agreement on that point. The second question is whether the alternative of loosening prices (and thereby solving some of these supply problems by moving to a free market) does not run the risk of causing political repercussions.

I think that both of those are closely related—that the question is essentially one of what the alternatives are—and I believe that one alternative is decontrolling now, which might produce somewhat higher prices in the very short run, but would produce lower prices in the long run. On the other hand, we could decide to hold prices down in the very short run. There would then be some immediate shortages, and this would absolutely guarantee higher prices in the medium and long run. I think these are the real alternatives that we face.

JILL SCHUKER, New England Congressional Caucus: There has been a lot of talk this afternoon about reliance on the market, and the question is: What is that? Right now does that not really mean meeting the OPEC price? I just suggest this in passing. We talk a lot about increasing oil and gas supply and certainly this is important: I think we are all in agreement on that. But what happens if OPEC— and I guess we are talking about the Saudis in this case—knocks down the price to $4.00 or $5.00 a barrel, or something similarly reasonable? What happens, then, to all this talk about going in the direction of more exploration and building up our own supplies?

I do not know if such an action is a live possibility, but it is something that could be carried out as a matter of strategy on OPEC's part. In order for us to escape from being the prisoner of OPEC—which is where I think the present policies have brought us—we must allow a decent return on capital and a sufficient price to allow for exploration of domestic reserves, no matter what the international price of oil does. Otherwise we will be right back again in the same dependency. Let us say OPEC dropped the price way down. Then everyone would breathe a sigh of relief and say "the energy crisis is over," but if in the long run that led to our becoming 50 percent instead of 30 or 25 percent dependent on foreign oil, and then the price shot back up to a level higher than at present, where would we be? We can not let such a possibility change our real attitude toward moving toward national independence for our energy supply.

JIM BISHOP: I think Ms. Schuker has touched a very important point, because one part of the U.S. energy policy is the international part. Kissinger and Enders are going to Paris in December [1975] to cut a deal with OPEC. Out of that deal could well come a long-term assured supply and lower prices, or at least that is the intention. Somewhere along the way, the domestic approach and the international approach will have to be rationalized by the government: to my satisfaction, that has not yet been done.

69

Personally, I would be worried about the value of a deal, if it assumes a lower price and a supply from the OPEC nations, given OPEC's past behavior. I would really wonder what we would be getting in the deal, and whether they would rip the deal up in a year or two just as they did at Tehran four years ago. But that is where Secretary Kissinger and the State Department are headed—without any oversight, incidently, by the Congress, absolutely none at all.

DR. STAHR: The Council for Economic Development has been having discussions and debates leading to policy statements on energy, both domestically and internationally. One of the ideas that has emerged in those discussions has been that the government should—and there are two or three mechanisms for doing it—give a guaranteed price assuring a return on investment for the development of new sources, including new oil wells. If we really look like we are getting to be independent, then unless OPEC has disappeared or lost its mind entirely, it will lower the price of oil in time to head off our independence. OPEC does not want to see its best market suddenly disappear right from under its nose. With the danger of lower OPEC prices facing them, American investors just will not invest if there is a chance that just at the moment their investment is supposed to pay off, suddenly the bottom will fall out. One way or another, and we could go into the methods some other time, the government will have to support industry by making sure what the industry can expect in price.

MR. DiBONA: I would like to point to a little bit of history. We talked about the Import Quota Task Force earlier, and in their report, which incidentally very much underestimated the future demand for oil in the United States, the policy they recommended was to use tariffs to keep the import of non-Western Hemisphere oil below 10 percent. A flexible tariff was recommended. That report recognized this potential problem. The report is often cited for its other conclusions and because the recommendations were not followed. The numbers were wrong, the projections were wrong in the report, but they were the substance or the basis of the recommendations.

JUDGE LANGDON: What we would really be doing is coming back a full circle. This point would get back to our little debate with Ms. Schuker this morning, about whether the oil import program was a viable program, and whether its aims and goals were really those of national security.

Obviously if we attempt to develop our shale oil, our tar sands, our gasification and liquefaction of coal at high prices (assuming that perhaps this program that Vice President Rockefeller was discussing with us today would be initiated and we would commit several hundred billion dollars to such a program), the Arabs could decide, "We can scuttle that program by flowing in this very cheap oil." They could succeed—assuming this was their policy—if the public failed to recognize the national security importance of maintaining our own energy self-sufficiency. That is exactly what would happen.

MR. BLACKBURN: On natural gas, I do not have a handle on national figures as Mr. Nassikas has, but I am familiar with the costs of finding and producing. If there is to be a delivered price in the $2.00 to $3.00 area, there are vast untapped reserves that could be put into production and it would not be necessary to give any subsidy to get this done. But I would say that if there is going to be any of this kind of price guessing that has been talked about, one should sign a very short contract.

On Ms. Schuker's question about the reduction of price by the Middle East, I can tell what we did the last time it happened, when the price was $1.25 a barrel and we could not find oil at $1.25: We did everything that we could. We did get some protection from limiting imports. We could not compete. There were those who said that we ought to shut down strippers, and some who said we should shut down our entire domestic industry because we could not compete. It is fortunate, I think, that we did not do that.

MR. MILLER: I personally believe that a market solution is the best solution, but I think we have to temper it. After all, people have to live through the market solution. When DuPont and General Motors were broken apart, it was because they were not willing to live with the market solution at that time. They wanted the protection of the law so they could separate out their shares over a period of time. I suggest now that industry will have to recognize that a market solution, if it came immediately without some tempering, could cause drastic results.

I think I speak for several people here—and I look at Governor Boren, myself, Mr. Craven—when I say that there is a reservoir of resentment among the people in my generation who have grown up in different times from those who grew up during the Depression. We are the people who are becoming the majority in the country—and I do not say that as a "youth." But there is a generation gap and it is causing a lot of this bitterness. The failure to recognize this is going to exacerbate our problems.

The fact is that as soon as the question of government intervention is brought up by Vice President Rockefeller's suggestion that the government step in, there is an immediate abhorrent reaction to this, in and of itself. This reaction is going to lead to further problems. Indeed, the immediate reaction of many of my constituents is that they are against us: confidence in institutions is just not there anymore.

VERMONT ROYSTER, *Wall Street Journal:* Ms. Schuker stated my main point in a different way from the way I wanted to make it. The point is that if we could consider this purely as an economic matter, I personally would go entirely for the market solution. But it is a foreign policy matter as well as a domestic matter. In other words, if we could be sure that the world energy market would be a free market from here on out, then our best approach would be a free-market approach. But we are faced with a foreign policy problem that enormously complicates the situation.

MR. JONES: It is obvious that we are faced with an increasing need for energy in this country. It is also obvious that petroleum and natural gas are going to be the energy sources for the near future. The one positive thing we have to go on is the fact that this country is blessed with the most efficient and viable oil industry of any in the world. That industry stands ready to meet our need, if given the proper economic incentive. The necessary capital will be tremendous, and it must come, probably, from the government as well as from the consumer.

MR. MURPHY: As we close, I want to endorse resoundingly what Dr. Stahr had to say about the issue of external costs. A coal mine ought to be looked at just like the producing well that Judge Langdon or Ray Sutton would not allow us to operate because it would put the oil-field brine in a stream. If the coal mine cannot stand the cost of restoring the soil, even though it might be located in the Monument Valley where the land has zero surface value for any known economic use, it would just not be economical, and we should do without it.

GOVERNOR BOREN: I very much appreciate the tenor of the discussion. I think we have come to some points of agreement. Maybe I am an optimist, though I guess you have to be if you want to be a governor these days or indeed hold any public office. But what I have heard around the table is support for a market solution, as far as incentives through price are concerned and as far as allocation of a scarce and precious resource is concerned.

We have also heard that we must consider the external costs and the environmental impact, as well as the scarcity, as a part of the true cost. We have also heard that we cannot look at this purely as an economic problem without looking at the foreign policy implications and the need for national self-sufficiency and some built-in protections to insure that, since we are not dealing with a purely economic problem.

We have also heard that, for practical political reasons and because of hardships that will fall more heavily on one region or another, the market mechanism, while it will be used to get us out of this problem, may need to be tempered to a degree when we get down to something like propane or something like fuel oil or something else to ease temporary dislocations and also, perhaps, to phase in the market mechanism. It should begin to work, but as painlessly as possible, even though we know that it cannot work without some pain.

Again, without wanting to sound like a repeat of some of Secretary Simon's speeches, I would say that from whatever region we come we must also face the fact that to develop energy, no matter what kind of energy, in the short run or the long run, will require a tremendous amount of capital investment. This means being honest with the American people and saying that we must sacrifice something that would be spent somewhere else right now in order to induce capital investment to create the energy we need. I think that we must deal honestly with that overriding problem, too.

PART FOUR

Energy Policy:
A New War Between the States?

In the final session of the conference, regional political leaders (Governor Boren and Senator Brooke), representatives of government and environmentalists (Administrator Zarb and former Secretary of the Interior Udall), and a well-informed audience discussed whether energy issues would indeed be the cause of regional divisiveness. The discussion was videotaped for educational and commercial TV and the edited transcript that is presented here has been published separately as an AEI Round Table.

ROUND TABLE DISCUSSION

MELVIN LAIRD, moderator of the Round Table: During the past two days, we have had a conference here in Washington to discuss regional interests and the national interest in the energy problems of the United States. In our panel discussion today, we want to discuss some of the problems that confront the states, in what some have entitled "The Energy War Between the States."

As Senator Brooke knows, Massachusetts and some of the New England states have been criticized from time to time in the Congress by representatives of Texas and Louisiana for refusing to take environmental risks in developing their own energy sources in the New England area, particularly for failing to develop offshore drilling and refinery capacity. I would like to ask him for his comment.

SENATOR BROOKE: You refer, of course, to the old battle of the producer states and the consumer states. Of course, during the Industrial Revolution, everyone suffered. We consumer states had our problems and the producer states had their problems. At that time, we were not so conscious of earth, of the environment, as we are today. I think we are all to blame. I think we ought to be not so much concerned with the past as with the future. We New Englanders are ready to take our risks. We may have to take our risks in Massachusetts as well, because we may have great resources of coal in southeastern Massachusetts, and we may have some gas in the outer continental shelf. We want to develop those resources, but we do not want to make the mistakes that have been made in states like Louisiana and Texas and around the Gulf of Mexico. We want to do it with environmental protection.

You know, we did have a refinery in Everett, Massachusetts. That refinery, as I recall, was closed down by the major oil company. Then we tried to get a refinery in Machiasport. And what happened? The producers and the refiners came up and testified against it. I think it was Secretary Udall's administration that really killed it, as a matter of fact, and we would have been very happy to have had it in New England. We want to develop the deep water ports; we want to develop a refinery; and we will do it, so long as we can be sure that our environment will be protected. We are also willing to compensate those states that have suffered—the Gulf of Mexico areas. In the Coastal Zone Act, for example, I cosponsored and supported an amendment which would compensate them for the past, the recent past, and enable them to rezone for the future.

MR. LAIRD: Secretary Udall, you were in charge of administering a very important program when you were secretary of the interior in the Kennedy and Johnson administrations—the Mandatory Oil Import Program. In our discussions yesterday, we heard some criticisms of the program—of what it was intended to do, what it actually did, and whether it really accomplished what it was intended to accomplish. What is your comment about the program, as the person charged with the responsibility of administering it during a very important period?

MR. UDALL: First, recall that there was a worldwide free market in oil until 1957. The Arab-Israeli War of that year and the closure of the Suez Canal produced a crisis. Out of that crisis came the U.S. oil import program which, for the first time, began to pit consumer states against producer states because it put a lid on oil imports into the United States. The program ran from President Eisenhower's administration until 1973, and I administered it for eight of those years.

Second, I always had mixed feelings about that program because it meant that New England, as Senator Brooke well knows, was paying through the nose to protect the producer states. I think the New England states paid about a half billion dollars a year extra because they could not get cheap oil from the Middle East. Now, even though at the time it seemed to me this was unfair, when the Arab embargo came along two years ago, I could see that if we had not had an oil import program, if we had not limited that penetration of the United States, we might have been importing 75 percent of our oil instead of only 36 percent. The oil industry in the producing states might have been in such a predicament that it would not have been able to provide what the country needed.

These are very complicated problems but there is one general point I have to make. The one great lesson I learned in the eight years I was in government is that it will be a great mistake if we ever balkanize, if we ever have regional feelings in this country that are so intense that we cannot have a national energy policy. Our country's great strength is the fact that we use our resources in a rational way to benefit the whole country. The regions of our country are connected by pipelines carrying oil and natural gas. This conflict between producer and consumer states can be destructive and damaging to the country if we do not bring it under control.

MR. LAIRD: Governor Boren, it was not too many years ago that we used to hear the oil producers in the United States say, "You get us $5.00 a barrel for oil and the problems are all over." Now the price has gone beyond $5.00 a barrel, and the problems are not over. What is the answer to that?

GOVERNOR BOREN: One answer is that at the depths where we are finding oil, the production costs have increased tremendously. What we have to do—and I agree with what has been said—is to quit drawing a distinction between producing and consuming states. In fact, Oklahoma in a very short time will be an importer of energy, a consuming state. Oklahoma's interests, like those of the rest of the nation, lie in seeing more domestic sources of energy of all kinds developed. And we all have to consider what is going to happen in this country in the next three to four years, as well as in the next ten. We talk about development of nuclear power, solar power, offshore exploration, but these things take time. Capital investments have to be made; environmental impact studies have to be made; true costs, environmental and otherwise, have to be estimated. We must consider what can be done in the short run to solve the problem of the next three to four years so that our economy holds together while we make these long-term decisions.

I think that the answer in the short term has to come from two sources of energy that are readily available—oil and gas. In each case we have pipeline networks so that as soon as a well is drilled and the oil or gas enters the pipeline, it can get to the places that need it—it can flow into areas like Massachusetts or North Carolina to keep the factories open through winter and to keep unemployment down. But the only way we can get oil and gas developed in the short run is to have a price that is adequate. I heard one governor explain this recently by saying, "If the price of candy bars in this country was set at two cents a bar and the cost of producing a candy bar was eighty-nine cents, we would have a candy bar shortage." That puts it very simply, but it is true. As long as we hold the prices of oil and gas to levels below what it costs to produce oil and gas, there will not be enough oil and gas produced. We must have a reasonable price structure, and I think we can reach national agreement on this. The governors, for example—thirty of them—have endorsed a compromise plan. I think we did very well to get thirty governors to agree on anything. It shows what can be done. And only three of them were from producing states; twenty-seven were from consuming states, some from New England. What we agreed upon was a five-year suspension on natural gas regulation, during which period new natural gas would be allowed to be sold at a market price that would make exploration possible. New production requires deep wells, and some of these cost $5 or $10 million apiece. By limiting the suspension to a five-year period, we protect the consumer—in New England for example—against a rapid increase in prices.

Solutions can be found. People in our part of the country, in the so-called producing region, know that there are problems that have to be eased—for example, special problems with propane users and with home fuel oil in Massachusetts. Trade-offs will have to be made, and I think that as long as people are of good will, the trade-offs can be made.

SENATOR BROOKE: Governor, can we not have an equivalent cost for oil and gas?

79

GOVERNOR BOREN: I think, senator, we will have equivalent prices for all sources of energy ultimately. But we must remember that all forms of energy are precious. For example, if natural gas is really worth $2.00 and we let it be priced twenty cents lower in some contracts, what do we encourage? We encourage people to think that natural gas is cheap and we thereby encourage them to use it wastefully. We are wasting a precious natural resource through the pricing structure. I agree with that.

My objection to the Stevenson bill, for example, and to some other proposals that have come up in this area, is they would require an average price of natural gas of, say, $1.30 per Mcf. Now, that price may be fine as an average, but it would not be good as a price for new natural gas, because it costs much more than $1.30 to find new natural gas below 15,000 to 20,000 feet.

SENATOR BROOKE: That is not an arbitrary figure. The Joint Economic Committee—Paul MacAvoy—they have models that show that $1.30 per Mcf, and, I think, $9.00 for a barrel of oil are generous. We want to have incentives for production: what we would like to see is simply an equivalent price with a ceiling that would encourage production.

GOVERNOR BOREN: The problem is that ceilings will not encourage production. Let me explain it this way. My energy council had a study of a utility company done by a nationally known C.P.A. firm. This council, by the way, is not an industry group, but an impartial group with consumer representatives on it. The study showed that the residential user in New York was paying $2.60 per unit for natural gas. Out of that $2.60, do you know what the amount paid to the Oklahoma producer was? Twenty-five cents. The rest of it was pipeline cost, sixty cents, and distribution cost in New York, $1.75. I would not be opposed to raising the average price of natural gas from twenty-five cents to $1.30, though I do not think you have to raise the average price of natural gas that high to get results. The average could in fact go up to fifty or sixty cents, and production would still be encouraged, because the old contracts would still be held in force. But here is the key. In Oklahoma the new gas needed to fill those pipelines is down below 15,000 feet. Shallow wells are relatively cheap to drill, but below 15,000 feet and down to 20,000 and 30,000 feet, it may cost $2.00 to get that new gas. If the price is pegged at $1.30, there will not be any new gas, although $1.30 average would be generous on the old gas. We have to draw a distinction between the price per unit of the new gas we are going after now, which is expensive, and that would be a fair average price for natural gas.

SENATOR BROOKE: I think there will be a fair distinction drawn.

MR. LAIRD: Could we have your comment on that, Frank?

MR. ZARB: I think both the senator and the governor hold the same fundamental philosophy, but when it comes to the hard chore of setting out the numbers, they are not very close together. The governor is saying that gas to replace this twenty-five cents per unit gas, will oftentimes cost $1.00 or $1.75 at the wellhead, and that we will have to pay this $1.00 or $1.75 so that the exploration can take place.

When the senator talks about equalizing the price of gas and oil, he is referring to something that is now being studied in the Senate. While the notion has some merit, the numbers are currently set at a point that in our judgment would not promote the desired production of more American supplies of gas and oil. If the numbers were set correctly, that equilibrium formula or any other formula of that kind certainly could do the job. But the big questions are where we set the numbers and whether we let the costs escalate over a period of time to reflect increased costs.

It really comes down to the bottom line. If the people are willing to pay for new American oil and gas, supply will be assured and we will not have to pay outrageous oil and gas prices to foreigners. But the people are going to have to agree on a price: that is the point on which the debate must take place and one hopes the result will be legislation that is realistic but not excessive.

MR. LAIRD: Yesterday in our discussion several comments were made to the effect that a growing distrust has developed not so much of the producing areas of the country as of the oil industry as a whole. As the chief energy officer of our government, what do you think about this growing distrust of the oil industry that has shown up in the various polls and public opinion surveys in the United States?

MR. ZARB: I would say two or three things about that. First, I would be the last to defend some of the actions of the industry in past years or some of its current practices. I think that the oil industry, like many of our other larger institutions, in both private and public life, has a long way to go to earn back the respect of the American people. And that respect has to be earned: it cannot be talked back into existence. The industry must take its share of the blame, along with the rest of us, for creating the problem we currently have. As a nation, we all sold out to cheap oil. And while the import quotas were pointed in the right direction, even if they were incorrectly motivated at the time, they did not really get the job done. New England sold out to cheap oil along with the rest of us and now they are about 80 percent dependent upon foreign source oil.

Finally, I would say that the most unhappy conclusion to be drawn from our experience with the energy crisis is how frequently a politician will take a set of circumstances like these—our suspicion of big institutions, some of the past problems that have developed and even some of the current practices—and use it in an "evil spirit" theory. The politicians will imply to the American people that if we could only find a way to exorcise the evil spirit, all of our problems would be solved. Of course, the claim is fraudulent; the problems are real; but they should be corrected, not "exorcised." The industry should be examined with other institutions and it should be held accountable to the people, but no one should try to convince the people that if only we can get rid of the evil spirit, we will find a big pool of oil or gas at the end of the rainbow and all will be well again. Politicians who would play on that desire for the rainbow's end are doing a disservice to all of us.

MR. LAIRD: Can we determine whether there is a real understanding of what the increased prices brought about by OPEC mean to the consumer in the United States? Certainly no understanding of this sort shows up in any of the public opinion surveys. I have seen Mr. Zarb speak up strongly about a 10 percent increase, but I have not heard him speak strongly about the 500 percent increase.

MR. ZARB: I want to start now. I was particularly incensed about two things: first, I was incensed that the nation sat around the tickers for three months waiting to see how much more OPEC was going to charge the American consumers. Eventually, when we learned that we were only going to have to pay $2 billion a year more, some among us said "My goodness, it could have been worse." I was incensed about that. Prices went up not 500 percent but 700 percent before this latest increase and, that in itself, is an outrage.

I think our outrage should be directed as vigorously internally as it is externally. We, as a nation, have sat for ten years, doing nothing, even though there have been a number of studies both private and governmental warning us that we were getting into deep trouble. We have allowed the conditions that permitted OPEC to charge these prices. For the last year, with all the argument that has been raised, we have not produced one solid piece of legislation to fix things. I would think that we should be as angry both at what OPEC does and its irrational and unreasonable changes in price in the last two years, and at our own inability to come to grips with the situation.

MR. UDALL: I have the feeling that, from an energy standpoint, we in this country are still living in a dream world. We have all this talk about energy independence, yet month by month, week by week, we are becoming more dependent on outside sources of energy. I do not think we are facing the realities. As Mr. Zarb has just said, OPEC's power is undiminished—indeed, I think OPEC is stronger today than it was before. We have acted as though there were some way that we could undo the cohesion that makes OPEC's actions possible. Moreover, we have gotten ourselves deeper in the hole because we have failed to recognize that even if we gave the petroleum industry everything it asked for—I wish some of the oilmen would admit this—even if we gave the industry complete decontrol, the industry still could not maintain our reserves and our present production.

Other than the topsoil in this country, our petroleum is probably the most precious resource we have, and we are running out of it. There is no quick way— in fact, there is no way at all—that the oil industry, if it did its very best, could significantly increase production in this country. Once we recognize that, we can see how deep is the trouble we are in. We will have to conserve and stretch and wisely use all the remaining oil and natural gas that we have.

SENATOR BROOKE: I think the key is in the word "conserve." If we are ever going to be free of OPEC, or at least not as dependent as we are on OPEC, we must have a tough conservation policy. With due respect to Mr. Zarb, we do not have a tough conservation policy. Take the conservation of gasoline: we still have the big inefficient cars. From 1974 to 1975, when we were supposedly conserving, we increased the use of gasoline by 3 percent.

Now, in our region, we have cut back in some areas. We cut back 20 percent on home heating fuel, and we cut back 18 percent on industrial use of residual oil. But no one in the nation, including us, cut back on gasoline. We have not done it, but we are going to have to bite the bullet. One possibility is the gasoline tax. Now, no one wants to talk about the gasoline tax, and some believe it would not work. When I came out with a twenty-cent tax on gasoline, you should have seen the mail I received. To get any support in the Senate, I had to lower my proposed tax to 15 cents.

Of course, a gasoline tax alone does not make a tough conservation policy: there are other factors that have to be built in. We will need conservation standards in our construction codes. I want the government to come up with a tough conservation policy even though I think that most of the policies the government has come up with so far have been wrong insofar as New England was concerned. The oil import tax hurt New England, indeed. Any artificial barrier has hurt New England going all the way back to 1938 when natural gas was first regulated. We suffered—as consumers, we suffered—while the producer states did relatively well. The measures were supposed to help the consumer, but they really did not help us in New England because we could not get natural gas at all.

GOVERNOR BOREN: That is a good point. When you talk about decontrol, people tend to think, "That's what the producer states want," but we are doing quite well under the present system. We want decontrol so we can send gas to you and get it produced for you in Massachusetts.

SENATOR BROOKE: We certainly do not get it now. Indeed, we use hardly any natural gas for industrial purposes in New England. We have had to use high-cost oil for industrial development in our New England states and we have had to go overseas to get it. We are getting cheap oil and then, of course, the government put in import quotas and then OPEC came in, and now we are paying more than anyone else for oil.

GOVERNOR BOREN: I agree. Secretary Udall has talked about conservation and I agree that we have to conserve. But, on the other hand, it is not easy for us to go to the American people and say, "All right, cut back drastically on your use of energy consumption. Keep your car in the garage. Turn the thermostat down." I think that if the American people can be convinced that they must really do these things, they will do them. I think we are a tough people and willing to make hard sacrifices once we understand the necessity for them. But I think the people have trouble believing that there is a necessity.

In Oklahoma right now, if we had the right kinds of government policies, by going in and forcing water down into the ground into our old oil wells, we could recover in five to ten years 5.2 billion barrels of oil in Oklahoma alone. Now, think for a moment about that figure of 5.2 billion barrels. Our present annual production of oil is 130 million barrels. We have over $250 million available to go into drilling natural gas wells in western Oklahoma right now, but held back because of uncertainty. After all, why would anyone invest in a well when they do not know what the price is going to be and they do not know if there will be a positive return on their investment? When we do not use the reserves we have available right now because of uncertainty caused by governmental policies, I question the governmental policies, even though I think the administration is try to bring some certainty to the industry. If we could have that certainty, and if the people could know that we would be getting every available ounce of production, I think the people would be willing to make sacrifices. But I think we have to be honest. If we are going to have more energy in this country, we will have to invest dollars in exploration for new energy and in developing nuclear energy, solar energy, the environmentally clean sources of energy. We will have to invest money in development, and this means that the people will have to give up spending money on some other things. I believe that if we tell the people the truth, they will be willing to conserve, willing to invest to get as much energy as we can, and then we will be off dead center.

MR. UDALL: I guess it was at the conference that AEI held a year ago that Mr. Laird came out for gasoline rationing. What he said was that "sooner or later a tough gasoline-rationing system is going to be needed in the United States."[1] I agree the only way that the United States can send a message to OPEC loud and clear is to go to some kind of rationing. What I would like to have agreement on here is that the producing states' spokesmen and the people from the industry are incorrect to say, "If you just rip off the lid and let us have these high prices, we will produce more and the crisis will be over because we will increase production." It will not happen. The year 1974 was a very interesting year. The oil industry had everything it asked for, and the industry invested $4 billion more in 1974 than in 1973. Drilling increased 23 percent in 1974. But

---

[1] Edward J. Mitchell, ed., *Dialogue on World Oil* (Washington, D. C.: American Enterprise Institute for Public Policy Research, 1974), p. 26.

in 1974 we used 3.5 billion barrels of oil, while the oil industry found only 2 billion barrels of oil. We used 21 trillion cubic feet of natural gas in 1974, while the industry found only 8 trillion cubic feet. Our natural gas reserves have been declining since 1968, and our crude oil reserves have been declining since 1961. The picture is one of an industry that has passed its peak, and a resource that is limited. We are on the down-side of the curve, and pretending that there is some way we can raise production back up. If I could get agreement that we have passed the peak, then we would really get into conservation. I agree with you that we have to have incentives, that prices will have to go up, and the consumer will have to pay whatever it will take.

SENATOR BROOKE: We have been paying. But I do not think we can be sure that we have passed the peak, we can only guess that we may have passed it.

MR. UDALL: I am convinced that we have all the evidence necessary on that.

MR. ZARB: I would like to speak on a few of the issues raised. First, I want to correct the record on gasoline. As a practical matter we have had fairly flat gasoline consumption in the last three years. Last year and this year consumption has been just about the same, partly as a result of the recession. The latest automobiles announced even by the American manufacturers, who are used to producing chromium-plated gunboats instead of cars, are being aimed at good mileage. I think this came about because the consumer exercises his vote in the showroom. The price of gasoline has increased as a result of OPEC's actions, and now the consumer asks "How many miles per gallon?"

Second, let us talk for a moment about this word "conservation." I think we must examine what we mean by conservation and what we are going to need to achieve conservation. The first question, the obvious one, is whether conservation means that we are to price this scarce commodity at its real value to the economy and to society. If we price the resource below its real value, its replacement value (which is one notion that ought to be examined), we cannot hope to have society place its true value on it. The way we build our homes, the way we build our automobiles, the way we run our factories, depends on how we treat this scarce resource. When we had gasoline at 19.9 cents per gallon and gave away six empty glasses with a full tank, we were in chromium-plated gunboats. Each year we had more chrome and more horsepower—each year more gasoline was consumed.

With due respect to Senator Brooke, in this area of conservation, I have reached the point at least of mild irritation. There were conservation bills sent to the Congress last January that I considered extremely important, bills that had no concern with the price of energy. One was a fundamental piece of legislation that had to do with how we build our buildings. The President asked the Congress for a standard housing and construction code for all building throughout the nation.

It was a simple piece of legislation, providing that any builder who wanted a mortgage from a bank that had a federal relationship had to have a certificate indicating that he had followed a very narrow range of thermal standards. I talked to the architects, the builders and the labor unions, and I thought we had a general understanding that this was the right direction to go in. That legislation has been up there now for ten months, and I am told we are not going to get the bill, certainly that we are not going to get the mandatory provisions of the bill.

Our authority to require the utilities to convert from gas and oil to coal is important, because (as Governor Boren mentioned a moment ago) we waste natural gas, and the most magnificent way to waste natural gas is to burn it to generate electricity. Now our authority to require that conversion has been before the Congress since this past spring. The provisions expired in June, and the Congress is reluctant to renew them.

Here are two important ways of forcing more effective use of our natural resources that the body politic is apparently not yet ready for. This is not merely a New England matter. I am speaking now in national terms. When we talk about conservation, we should really "put up or shut up." Yet the Congress did not go along with the gasoline tax: the House defeated it by an enormous margin.

SENATOR BROOKE: The gasoline tax was not popular, there is no question about that. Now, our citizens are not going to be able to burn coal in Chicago and Detroit and Cleveland and the major cities across the country, because coal is not clean. We have environmental problems that we have to resolve, and apparently we are not able to resolve them quickly. I know that Congress is partly at fault. I think Congress has a responsibility to resolve the problem—even when it is not a case where it can simply be said, "We require the use of coal for utility purposes," and all of a sudden everyone answers, "We will use coal." The coal must be clean in order for it to be used by the utilities.

MR. ZARB: Before our authority expired in June, we had issued orders to twenty-five utilities. The law provides for an Environmental Protection Agency veto if our analysis of environmental considerations is not correct, and within that context, we still have a long way to go to get our job done. Indeed, in many ways, we cannot do the job. Of course, Chicago is moving forward with nuclear power: it is going to settle its problem a different way. The point I am trying to make is that, while some people express a lot of concern about pricing (and I happen to consider pricing as the responsible mechanism for allocating our natural resources in this country) and while the same people also express a lot of concern about conservation as a national policy, I keep asking them, "Where is the body politic that is ready to pass laws that will require conservation?" I have given the simplest of examples, building standards; it seems to me these are surely something we could agree on, but we are obviously not going to get the legislators to do so.

MR. UDALL: I think Mr. Zarb has a legitimate complaint that Congress has been slow to act on conservation. The slowness is part of this popular belief that there is some easy way out, that we do not have to make basic structural changes. We talked about gas rationing, but I would like to ask what kind of gas rationing we are going to have if we cannot pay the bill for imported oil at all? The only way we have been paying the bill for imported oil is by producing food that we can export: we are earning over $20 billion by selling farm products, and we are paying an oil bill of $30 billion. When we cannot pay that oil bill, the President, whoever he may be, will have to lay it on the line to the American people: if we are to have gasoline at all, rationing will be severe. The big changes that could be made—and it is in making them that we will begin to move towards conservation—are changes in our transportation priorities. Let us begin by putting more money into mass-transit systems, so that instead of my getting in my own car and struggling for forty-five minutes through Washington traffic to get to this conference, I would have an easy and convenient way to get here, by railroad. Railroads are intrinsically enormously efficient. The restoration of the railroads could help solve the energy crisis by conserving on energy consumption and, incidentally, providing more jobs.

GOVERNOR BOREN: Let me get back to the fact that natural gas is the fuel most readily available to help save us in the present crunch—and also the cleanest fuel, and environmentally the least harmful. When are we going to hear from the conservationists some strong support for realistic pricing policies to get the natural gas we have out of the ground to help solve the current problem?

When I hear that the conservationists are saying to the American consumer, "Look, we are going to do everything we can. Let us put every bit of capital investment we can into getting as much of these clean fuels as we can. Let us put in all the capital investment that we can to develop new sources of energy," then I will be willing to say to the people of my state in Oklahoma, "We will get tough for conservation, and we will look at these other alternatives." I think we ought to hear constructive proposals for both sides, but from the conservationists I only hear talk about limiting use, and from the producers I only hear talk about increasing production. When are we going to hear the conservationists call for incentives for more production of clean fuel?

SENATOR BROOKE: We will do that. But the problem is that we just cannot agree on numbers. I gave $9.00 and $1.30, and Governor Boren did not accept those figures. I gave the authority for it, the studies that have been made, and Mr. Zarb does not accept that authority. The Senate Budget Committee came up with the conclusion that these proposals would give a 14 percent return on the investment for the oil companies.

GOVERNOR BOREN: I will make a deal with Senator Brooke. If he will take that $1.30 as an average price—if he will let us keep the old prices controlled and let the new prices go up to encourage exploration—we will keep the average below the $1.30.

SENATOR BROOKE: I am a Republican, and I believe in free enterprise; I believe in the profit system. We must have gas and we must have oil at a reasonable price, and there has to be a fair profit. That is what we are trying to achieve, right?

GOVERNOR BOREN: Right.

SENATOR BROOKE: And there must be an incentive for production. We want to have that incentive, but we want to have that reasonable price, too. I have heard talk of our having a free market, but we do not have a free market: the OPEC cartel establishes the prices. We cannot kid ourselves about that.

MR. ZARB: In fairness to the conservationists, let me say that they (at least privately, and to some extent in their own personal presentations around the country) have supported a price level consistent with the level I think is correct. They have not really done much on the Hill, but since they have other fish to fry, I can understand that. Even so, their figures are fairly consistent with the figures that we have in our thirty-nine-month plan. Now that plan really solved all the questions just raised, though in it we did not try our strength with OPEC, and we had a ceiling on domestic prices: in the first year, during a period of tender economic recovery, we had no price escalation. The plan answered all the substantive arguments of the people who were worried about the non-free-market condition, at least during this period, but we did not get the plan accepted for reasons I consider more political than substantive.

MR. LAIRD: I think it was a communications issue. As moderator, perhaps I should not comment here, but I do not think there were very good communications in this country on that thirty-nine-month plan.

MR. ZARB: I think that is a fair criticism. We had five days before a congressional recess to get the word out, and I will have to say that poor communications in those five days were a big part of the failure. On the other hand, it was fairly clear to most of us who were watching the vote-taking that even those Democrats who had indicated that they would support such a program switched their votes at the last minute, after nose-to-nose discussion. In one sense, there was more communication than I would have liked to have seen.

MR. UDALL: I accept Governor Boren's criticism and I think the conservationists in this country have to recognize that we should not be using a resource as precious and valuable as natural gas as a fuel as much as we are today, we should be saving it for raw materials. And part of the reason for our increased use is price. If we allow prices to rise, the people back down the line will have an adequate price, so that they can stay in business and find more gas.

The point I want to make, though, is that we cannot kid the consumer, and we must not kid ourselves. Even if prices reached the highest level that the oil industry wants, we would still probably see a slow decline in the supply of natural gas. In fact, that has already started: the trend is there. And that is why I think our being honest with the American people should eventually bring them to the point where they will say, "There is no easy way out. We are going to have to pay higher prices. We are going to have to conserve." The oil industry will have a real struggle to keep the curve of the decline from falling rapidly. This is the picture I see, and I may be wrong, but I think what we are having now may be the kind of dialogue that will help get us home.

GOVERNOR BOREN: I think this dialogue will help get us home, but I also think we can do much more in the area of production than we are doing. Our natural gas reserves within the state of Oklahoma have not declined: they have gone up 1 percent in the last four years. There is hope for new sources of production in the short term. But we must be honest all the way around: we will need tough conservation measures and we will need to invest in finding new sources of energy. And I do not think we should sell the American economy or our resourcefulness short: in the long run we can explore solar energy and nuclear energy, and other sources as well. Let us be really truthful with the American people, and tell them what the costs of failure here will be. If we do not invest enough money in energy exploration, if some day we do not have energy to run the plants and the factories, we are going to have 19 or 20 or 25 percent unemployment in this country. The people of this country are going to have to do without some of the things they now have, not only for the sake of conserving energy, but in order to get the money invested to explore new energy sources that will save their jobs in the long run. This is of vital importance.

SENATOR BROOKE: In New England, at least, we are going to have to do something much sooner than that for unemployment. In Massachusetts we have 13.9 percent unemployment already, and some pockets of 17 or 18 percent. Unemployment is 11.9 percent for all of New England. The cost of energy is so high in New England that it restricts, even prohibits, industrial development.

MR. LAIRD: But does the public really tie up the job problem with the energy crisis? When we look at these opinion polls we see that jobs are not tied up with the energy crisis in the public mind.

SENATOR BROOKE: I think they are in New England, because the people there recognize that we have lost industry—lost jobs—because of the high cost of energy.

Our utility prices are so high that a good number of people now are paying more for their electric bills than they are paying for their mortgages. Part of the reason is that our utility plants are burning residual oil, which is the highest priced oil. Eventually, we will have to get to a point where our utilities are no longer burning residual oil, but we have no cheap gas up there: we cannot burn cheap gas because the producing states do not send it to us.

GOVERNOR BOREN: Let me say that the producing states want to send it, and at a price lower than the proposed average. As I pointed out a while ago, of this $2.60 utility bill in Brooklyn, only twenty-five cents was going to the producer in Oklahoma and only sixty cents was even going to the pipelines. Now the pipelines cost billions of dollars, and if they are half full or less than half full, the consumer will have to pay more of the head cost on each delivered Mcf than if the pipelines are full. If the price at the wellheads went up to $1.30—or even less— the new gas will come in, those pipelines will be filled, and that fixed pipeline cost per Mcf reduced. Certified public accountancy studies show that if there were an adequate price at the wellhead, there would be adequate supply at lower cost to the residential user.

Let me say that I sometimes think the people in New England believe that the people in Oklahoma or Texas or Louisiana do not care about what happens to them. That is not true. The capital to start new businesses in Oklahoma comes from all over the United States. We have a national economy, after all. We have firms in Oklahoma that have their headquarters in North Carolina or in New York. The 16 percent or 11 percent unemployment in New England hurts Oklahoma a lot, because we are part of this national economy. Now, our producers in Oklahoma sat down with businessmen in North Carolina just last week, and the governors of the two states sat down, and we worked out a way we can get short-term gas to keep those textile mills in North Carolina operating. We want to help.

SENATOR BROOKE: Those textile mills in North Carolina are doing all right. They are taking all the textile business from New England, as a matter of fact.

MR. LAIRD: Now it's time to break off this discussion among the panelists and go to our audience. I notice that in our audience there are a number of listeners who themselves have a considerable claim to expertise in the energy field, and I look forward to some good questions and good answers.

JUDGE LANGDON: When I look at a national panel like this where there is no representation from the largest oil- and gas-producing state in the union, it occurs to me that there will have to be some exercise in detente if we are going to get along. But I have a number of observations and one or two questions I would like to ask. I will take Stewart Udall first: he and I have been friendly adversaries over many years. Stewart mentioned that in 1974 there were no restraints on the oil and gas industry, that the industry drilled all the wells it wanted to, and that he could not find that production of reserves had increased at all. I would like to call his attention to the fact that you do not use 1975 data to estimate what reserves were found in 1974: there is a lag time of substantially more than a year.

The discoveries on the North Slope that were made in February 1968 are not yet onstream. Since the North Slope discovery was made, I have heard estimates that there may be ten billion barrels of oil up there, in known recoverable reserves, but since that oil field was found, Texas has produced more than ten billion barrels of oil that have gone into the economy of this country and the North Slope has yet to produce. I think that is significant.

In the intrastate market, Texas has changed from a shortage position to a surplus position in the last eighteen months. I said yesterday that the state of Texas, on a short-term basis, could furnish the rest of the nation with somewhere between 500 million and a billion cubic feet of gas per day. This is not surplus gas, but it is gas that could, on a 30- 60- 90- or 180-day basis, help relieve some of the problems in Massachusetts and some of the other states.

MR. UDALL: The point that I was making—and I read Judge Langdon's statistics, too—is that I do not believe the claim by the oil industry that somehow, if we just give the industry whatever prices the market will bear, then a flood of new production is going to come on. All the curves, the long-term trends, show that domestic reserves can only decline from here. We know what is happening in Texas: the Texas companies are producing seven, eight, ten times more each month, and new oil and gas is not being found. The easy oil has been found, and the easy fields developed. Governor Boren was just telling us that to find the new gas in Oklahoma, they go down 15,000 feet. I think the country is being misled, and if Judge Langdon and I disagree, we disagree.

JUDGE LANGDON: Governor Boren mentioned that in Oklahoma there were perhaps five billion barrels of oil that are known, that have been discovered, but that will not be taken out of the ground under present economic conditions. Simply speaking, it costs more to recover it than it is worth. In Texas, it is estimated we have a hundred billion barrels of oil like this, that might be recovered with some form of tertiary and secondary recovery methods, but only at a price higher than we have now. I do not know what the price would be.

MR. UDALL: As long as the oil industry continues to say to the country, "If we just had prices that were high enough, the shortage would go away," we will be living in a dream world where nobody has to conserve. In those circumstances, the country will not take the steps toward conservation that this panel has been talking about.

JUDGE LANGDON: I think that most members of the panel recognize the fact that a high price is going to have a conservation effect. But I want to talk about the time it will take before higher prices are reflected in additions to reserves—and that will not be in a year or even the eighteen months Mr. Udall used when he said he had not observed any increase in petroleum reserves as a result of increased drilling in 1974.

A second question I would like to ask is a regional and provincial one. Senator Brooke made the statement that Massachusetts has substantial coal reserves and that there is a substantial possibility of oil being found offshore. At what price do you think the people in Massachusetts would be willing to go out there and drill and explore for it? I would like to see a consortium of Massachusetts people, who may be now unemployed, forming a drilling company and drilling and exploring for their own resources there.

SENATOR BROOKE: I quite agree with you. We have those fossil fuel resources. We have coal, and I think we ought to explore for it, if we can get a fair price, though I do not know what that price would be. It is said that this might be clean coal, the best coal that can be found. If that is true, then we can use it ourselves, and I hope we will do that. I think we ought to explore the continental shelf, but we have an environmental problem with that exploration because tourism is one of our biggest industries. Those Texans come up to Martha's Vineyard and Nantucket, and enjoy them. If we destroy that tourism, we are eroding our economic base. But I quite agree that we must have—and I think the federal policy ought to encourage—regional exploration and development of deep ports and refineries, and we must have exploration for these energy resources. But I personally do not know what the price that provides a fair return would be.

MR. DiBONA: I would like to make an observation and then move on to my question, because the observation is related to the question. I think that it is nonsense for Secretary Udall to say that the petroleum industry had all of the conditions necessary for it to do the job in calendar year 1974. There are several reasons for my saying that. The first is that while about one-third of the natural gas that is currently heating this room came from offshore Louisiana and Texas, only 4 percent of the offshore Louisiana and Texas lands have in fact been put up for lease. The lands that the industry has not had made available to it could possibly be a prolific source of oil and natural gas. I have to say, in Mr. Udall's defense, that most of that gas is coming from leases that he in fact let when he was secretary of the interior. The second reason for my saying this is that natural gas still is controlled by the Federal Power Commission at 52 cents per thousand cubic feet, which is a fraction of the equivalent of the price of oil in this country. The final reason for my saying it is that most of the oil produced in the United States is controlled at significantly less than half the international price for oil.

92

There are significant possibilities for the extension of existing fields that will not in fact be extended under existing pricing policy controls. So it is hard for me to agree that the conditions were ideal. In spite of that, in 1974, for the first time in over ten years, the number of producing wells at the end of the year exceeded the number of producing wells at the beginning of the year. As Judge Langdon has said, this is a very long lead-time business. We do not see the effects of change quickly, in either direction.

Now, these observations bring me to my question. Is what we are discussing the effect of regional schisms in energy in this country, or is it even a conflict between consumer and producer interests? Does it not make sense, rather, to look at this as a conflict between the short run and the long run? It is entirely possible to hold down the price of anything in this country in the short run, and we have, in the short run, since 1954, held down the price of natural gas. The consequence in the long run is shortages and the use of higher priced alternatives: protection of the consumer from market forces is not possible forever. Does it not make sense, then, to look at this as a short-run versus long-run problem, rather than as a producer-consumer or regional problem?

SENATOR BROOKE: I think it does. I think it ought to be seen as a short-run and long-run problem. I do not believe this is a question of consumer versus producer. It has been said, and I think we all agree, that it is a national problem. I, for one, favor the re-regulation of natural gas. I think you are absolutely right that we cannot continue natural gas at the price we have had. We have had the lid on the price of natural gas since 1938, and there is no strong incentive for the exploration of natural gas in the country, even though we need natural gas. We in New England have suffered because of this federal policy, and I am sure it has hurt the rest of the country. But I am not in favor of taking the lid off without having some ceiling at the initial stages until we know where we are going. I do not want the consumer to be hurt dramatically after the initial decontrols go into effect. That is why I favor the $1.30 per Mcf price, initially. But, I think, after five years or so, we may have to let prices travel their course.

MR. ZARB: I think we are making some progress on this issue with respect to this question of price. It is clear that we are going to have to create a long-range program, so that investments can flow into exploration; and if we have the federal government looking at the price every eighteen months, we are not going to get that long-range investment. The question Mr. DiBona raises is a good one. I think regional issues are a second-level abstraction of the major question. And Senator Brooke is quite right in pointing out that there is high unemployment in New England in part because its residual oil is priced higher than residual oil anywhere else in the country. The fact is that 99 percent of that residual oil comes from abroad, and that, indeed, is the essence of the national problem. We are spending

$27 billion of American money to support the industry and the workers of other nations. If we spend a piece of that here for the production of American energy, that piece might go to New England, so that we could substantially reduce the current unemployment rate.

MR. STAHR: I very much appreciated Frank Zarb's pointing out something that is not well enough known, which is that the conservationists do believe our precious energy sources, particularly oil and gas, ought to be priced at something like their true value. The underpricing has led to waste that we never could afford—waste that we are just now beginning to recognize and that we certainly can no longer afford. Mr. Zarb said that the conservationists have not come forward as much as we might because we had other fish to fry, and I want to remind everyone that many of those other fish will be fried if we can get at the full cost of energy production, by which I am including the externalities, especially the environmental costs. I think all the costs ought to be considered with great seriousness, both from the short- and long-run point of view.

My question has to do with getting at the problem of gasoline consumption. We waste more energy in gasoline than in any other form. We have practically abandoned one of the most efficient transportation systems possible, the American railroads, which used to be by far the best in the world. We have turned to the superhighway, which encourages wasteful use of energy, as well as taking enormous amounts of energy to construct. I would like to ask what are the prospects of getting some kind of hold on the automobile? I realize there are special regional problems with automobile use, but I also realize, as Stewart Udall does, that we cannot have regional solutions. I would like to hear some opinions from this distinguished group on what we should do.

MR. ZARB: A few quick observations. We ought to be very careful about the mass transit solution. There are studies telling us that in some cities mass transit programs are going to use more energy than we will save by abandoning automobiles. I think we ought to be careful to find out how much energy we are going to save or waste with some of the mass transit programs. I would add that the railroads were all regulated in the public interest and look where they are. With that in mind, I think we ought to take a look at where we are going. The automobile in the United States is an institution, and I do not think we are going to eliminate it as the American way of transportation—even a major part of the American way of life—though I do believe that we need not have the kind of gunboats we have been used to. The main thrust ought to be at manufacturing automobiles that are a lot more efficient than the ones we have had. For the first time, now, two American-made cars are among the top five in results of Environmental Protection Agency mileage tests. This concern with efficiency has been brought about for two reasons: first, the American motorist now goes into the showroom knowing that gasoline costs sixty cents a gallon, and second, the American automobile manufacturers are aware that they have given up 20 percent of their market to foreign manufacturers, primarily for that reason.

The congressional approach to this up till now has been to create a matrix of excise taxes relating to horsepower or some other efficiency index. The reason Congress has not gotten very far is that when the congressmen have really looked around, and have brought in Republican economists and Democratic economists and "economy" economists, they have found that what is really going to make the difference is the American consumer. They found that whatever they legislate, its effect will be far outweighed by what the market dictates. For that reason, I was willing to accept the Ways and Means Committee proposal for a law in this area, knowing all along that by 1980 the law would look foolish.

MR. UDALL: I want to speculate on something. I think that when the next election is over, a year from now, whoever is President may very well find himself in a position where our balance of payments is out of whack and he will say to the American people, "Look, this problem is too big; we have to cut our oil imports; we have to send a message to OPEC. I am asking each one of you to go to a short-term program of gas rationing to get us through a transition. I am asking each one of you to use your car 20 percent less than you have been using it."

That would not be the end of the American way of life. As we saw in Vienna, OPEC is held together by bailing wire. Reduction of driving by 20 percent would represent a cut of $3 million a day in imports, and it might be the thing that would break this crazy artificial world system. Someone who is leading the country will have to tell the people, "We are going to have to make some sacrifices, we are going to have to change our habits. In a year or two or three, we will get by and make it around the corner."

SENATOR BROOKE: May I just mention two things. One is the question of rationing, which Mr. Udall has mentioned three or four times. Voluntary rationing would be fine, but I am vigorously opposed to mandatory rationing: I do not think it would work; I think it would be costly; I think that there would be a black market.

The other thing is the politics of the energy question. Certainly I have not always agreed with the administration's programs: after all, coming from New England, I have felt that we have suffered a lot and I think the New England congressional delegation has been united in its effort to get some relief. But at least the administration has done something and the Congress has not.

I think Frank Zarb is absolutely correct: the Congress has pussy-footed with this issue too long. Of course, at present we are suffering from presidential politics within the Congress, and that has hurt us tremendously. I will not get into the names, and I am speaking mostly of the Senate side, because I do not know the

House side that well. On the Senate side, we have so many candidates for President that it will be a miracle if we ever get an energy policy out of the Congress. At least the administration has a policy, and I hope that this presidential election will soon be over so that the nation can have a policy.

MR. NASSIKAS: It seems to me that there are two basic ways to attain domestic energy self-sufficiency in this country. One is through conservation—probably through end-use controls on the application of energy resources—and the other is through an increase in the domestic supply of all energy resources.

It seems to me that we cannot attack the natural gas problem—over which the Federal Power Commission has jurisdiction—as though it were the problem of an isolated energy resource unrelated to all other energy resources. I believe that we should have decontrol of natural gas and decontrol of oil, but with protective covenants imposed by the Congress to assure that consumers will be paying a rational price and that investors will be able to receive a reasonable return on their investment. Oil and natural gas should be treated by the Congress, I submit, as part of one single problem, not fractured with one treated as separate from the other. We have discovered 25 to 35 percent of our natural gas domestically in this country as a result of the search for oil.

We have a devastating oil shortage domestically as well as a shortage of gas. We import 40 percent of our oil, and even though the shortage is greater for natural gas, we import only 5 percent of our gas, largely from Canada. It seems to me that the resolution of this problem is to increase exploration and development in both oil and natural gas. We must develop all supplemental energy resources in this country—fossil fuels, nuclear, and the rest. If we are to develop our hydrocarbon resources in the form of gassified coal or liquefied coal, it is essential that there be a competitive market structure and that there be some guarantee of a reasonable return to the investors from investment in the development of those synthetic fuels. This is one of the major issues confronting the Congress and the administration. My question would be whether this panel believes that we will be politically able to resolve a problem which can only be resolved when government policies are established on a rational basis.

MR. LAIRD: Governor Boren is a straight-talking politician from Oklahoma, and he calls the shots the way he sees them. What do you think, David?

GOVERNOR BOREN: I think we absolutely must move to a political resolution, and I think we can do exactly what you are talking about. I think the dialogue that Senator Brooke and I have been having here on the side has gotten us very close to some fundamental agreement about protecting the consumer while permitting a fair rate of return on investment so that we will have some investment. That is exactly what we must have.

And you know, I think it is time that someone in the political leadership of this country stood up to those who call themselves "consumerists." There are a lot of people running around this country saying, "I am the friend of the consumer and as the friend of the consumer, I am in favor of holding the price paid to the producer so artificially low that I'm going to assure a long-range shortage."

MR. LAIRD: David, most of those people are running for President on your ticket.

GOVERNOR BOREN: Let me tell you that, whatever ticket they are on, they are not going to have my support, because they are not telling the people the truth, and they are false friends for the consumer. If they want to help the consumer, let them be honest enough to say, whatever political party they belong to, that the only way to help the consumer in this country, the only way to help the person who needs a job in New England or the southern states during this winter's gas curtailment, is to develop adequate incentives for production. You know, we are a public-spirited people, but I could not afford to go out and drill for gas at fifty cents if it cost me a dollar; I could not even afford to drill one well. But as Senator Brooke was saying, we can still build in some protection against abrupt dislocations for the consumer.

Here is what I cannot understand. We have done this with natural gas in the governors' conference. Thirty governors have agreed that at the local level we must have this energy for our people; we have agreed on a compromise proposal that will deregulate the new gas for a period of time and help protect against rapid increases on the average. I am wondering why the same thing cannot be done in Washington. Why is it that the governors find it politically possible to agree, even on the rough trade-offs that need to be made—for example, that there are some things we in Oklahoma have to give up to New England, that we have to help protect the consumer in the area of home heating oil and some things like that, and that we are willing to do our part—while the people in Washington have not been able to get together in this sensible way.

SENATOR BROOKE: I think we will. We can, we must, we will—in 1977.

MR. LAIRD: Is the time from now to 1977 too long a period to delay?

MR. UDALL: We are going to find out. I think Mr. Zarb can tell us what is going to happen in winter 1975–1976 on natural gas. Time will not wait, of course, but, as Senator Brooke says, the question is in the political arena where almost everything waits. It is particularly important for my friends in the oil industry who have been hitting me over the head this morning to understand why the question is waiting in the political arena. I spend part of my time around the country trying to knock down this belief that the energy crisis is contrived, that oil companies are

97

holding back the end of the rainbow somewhere in Texas or Oklahoma. The belief is not true and everyone knowledgeable in the area knows it is not true, but two-thirds of the American people still think the energy crisis is contrived. The politics of the question right now are that the President appears to be saying, "Let the price go up," which means to Democrats and consumerists that "we will give the oil companies a big bonanza and the consumers are going to be hit in the pocketbook." Admittedly, this is a simplistic way of arguing the issue—the problem is a lot more complicated than that—but it is the way the issue is being argued. The questions, "What is a fair price for natural gas?" and "How can it be phased in so that it does not hammer at the average citizen in this country?" are what Congress is concerned about. I am afraid we must continue to have meetings like this, making headway, even if slowly, so that the problem may be resolved; it will still be an issue in the election next year.

MR. ZARB: Unhappily I am in agreement with Senator Brooke. I do not think the point of the debate has at all been, how soon and how high? The governors came up with a compromise that had a very slow impact. Senators Bentsen and Pearson submitted a bill to the Senate and there was a lot of demagoguery directed against it. We have gone forward with phase-in programs that would have a very slow impact, and there has been demagoguery directed against them. I think the only way that Senator Brooke's 1977 date is going to be moved up—and I think it should be moved up because another embargo two years from now would really be horrifying—is for the American people to understand some of these truths and not let the candidate say what his staff worker just told him: "It is popular to go out and bang the oil industry on the head or the Administration on the head. So, without knowing what you are talking about, Mr. Candidate, get up there and speak to that point."

If the American people are no longer receptive to that kind of talk, the situation will turn around. And the issue has to be debated with the American people because, as things stand now, the political institutions will not debate it in any way that will lead to a resolution.

MR. LAIRD: That is what we are trying to do with these American Enterprise Institute programs and public policy forums—to get a dialogue going, to get information out to the public so that there is better understanding.

MS. MURPHREE: I am glad the panel finally got around to what we consider the real problem in energy, which is that the people do not know what the situation is. They are confused about the price of natural gas, the price of oil, the control price, the deregulated price, the phased price, the phased decontrol. People end up not really knowing which "expert" to believe because the experts are saying different things. What really helps the person out there to understand the energy problem is its hitting him in the pocketbook—when he asks himself, "How is it going to affect my job and my lifestyle?" We are trying to get information to the people so they can understand. The American Enterprise Institute's television programs are one way; the League of Women Voters tries to do it in a number of other ways.

I think the key—as Governor Boren and Mr. Zarb have said—is that we need to level with the people. And it seems to me that when the politicians are moving around the country, instead of their playing upon regional differences and exacerbating the situation, it would be good if they could somehow take a national approach to the issues and say, "We are all in this together; what hurts New England will also hurt Oklahoma or Texas or Louisiana, and what is beneficial for California will be beneficial for Florida." The same thing is true for the high unemployment in this country. Of course, unemployment is worse in some places than in others, but it is still a general problem and we seem to have no national policies for solving it.

My concern is how the federal government, including the Congress and the administration, is going to help people understand this? Certain kinds of educational programs are needed to help people understand that we are going to have to change lifestyles. As Mr. Udall has said, energy is going to run out someday: there will be a day of reckoning, because technology will not put it off forever. My question is this: what is the best way to help citizens understand the real problems, to help them understand that we are all in this together, to help put a damper on the sectional passions that seem to have been aroused?

MR. UDALL: Too much of the debate thus far has been irrelevant. The scape-goating of the oil industry—saying that it is the cause of the problem and that if it would just straighten up and fly right, the problem would go away—appalls me. Two years after the Arab embargo, two-thirds of the American people still do not believe there is a serious long-term energy crisis. I think we have to get the point across that there is a crisis. I believe that, up to now at least, the political dialogue has confused the people—indeed the administration has confused the people.

The belief that if we just let the price of anything rise, it will sort itself out and then new supplies of oil and gas will come flooding in is simplistic. We must have a lot more forums like this. I hope the campaign in 1976 will not be all emotion, because the American people must understand that this is probably the most serious domestic problem in the second half of the twentieth century.

MR. ZARB: I frequently hear members of Congress, after an exhaustive hour of discussion, remarking, "What you say makes sense, but I simply cannot vote that way because the people back home will not understand it." This seems to be one of the biggest political cop-outs in our history. Where does leadership begin and this kind of attitude stop? If you are asking for a chain of communication that I think will really work, it is a chain that begins when the politician goes back home and says, "People, this is the problem and here are the alternative ways to solve it." I do not expect the people will always agree with my chosen alternative, but at least be honest and truthful with them.

SENATOR BROOKE: I think the public usually gets what it demands, and that is what Mr. Zarb has been saying. If the people demand something, they will get it from their politicians. This energy problem has now been propelled into top priority. It is on the minds of most Americans; it certainly is on the minds of the members of Congress today. We have spent weeks and weeks on energy—and although we have not done enough about it, to be sure, it is being discussed and the people are aware of it. I think we have to focus more and more attention upon it, and I think organizations such as the League of Women Voters ought to continue to give it top priority treatment. And if we continue to do that, the public will become more educated. But when we start talking about Mcfs and Btus today, the people become confused. All they know is that energy is costing them more, they are getting less energy, and they want something done about it.

GOVERNOR BOREN: I think that the people are wanting something they are not getting from their leaders. We had a roadshow in Oklahoma not too long ago— the show about Harry Truman that is being done right now, and I think some of the lines have a lesson for us. He may have been right, he may have been wrong, but he shot straight and he never was in doubt. When someone gets up and says (to go back to my candy bar example), "We are the friends of the consumer. We are going to help you by setting the price of candy bars at two cents. We are going to ration them until they all run out, which will be next year"—when someone takes such a position, I think our political leaders ought to get up and say, "You are a phony."

We want prices that will produce gas and oil and new forms of energy, that will give us jobs that we can keep. That, in the long run, is what is going to help us. And I think that until we have the kind of leaders who are going to shoot straight and say, "We will make some tough choices; we will take money out of some programs where it now is and move it into investing to find new and clean energy," we are not going to get the problem solved.

MR. LAIRD: On behalf of Governor Boren, Senator Brooke, Frank Zarb, the Federal Energy Administrator, and former Secretary of the Interior Stewart Udall, as well as the American Enterprise Institute, I thank you.

PARTICIPANTS

William Baroody, *President, American Enterprise Institute*
Jim Bishop, Newsweek *magazine*
W. T. Blackburn, *Vaughey and Vaughey*
David Boren, *Governor of Oklahoma*
Edward Brooke, *U.S. Senator, Massachusetts*
Robert Cahn, *The Conservation Foundation*
Ruth Clusen, *League of Women Voters*
Marlow Cook, *Shook, Hardy, and Bacon*
Donald Craven, *Federal Energy Administration*
Charles DiBona, *Executive Vice President, American Petroleum Institute*
Pete Domenici, *U.S. Senator, New Mexico*
Michael Dukakis, *Governor of Massachusetts*
Richard Fairbanks, *American Enterprise Institute*
Charles Gentry, *Legislative Assistant to Senator Domenici*
A. V. Jones, *Jones Co., Ltd.*
Melvin Laird, *Chairman, National Energy Project, American Enterprise Institute*
Jim Langdon, *Texas Railroad Commission*
Martin Miller, *Chairman, Public Utility Commission of Vermont*
Edward Mitchell, *Director, National Energy Project, American Enterprise Institute*
Gwen Murphree, *League of Women Voters*
Charles Murphy, *Chairman of the Board, Murphy Oil Corporation*
John Nassikas, *Chairman, Federal Power Commission*
Endicott Peabody, *Americans for Energy Independence*
Nelson Rockefeller, *Vice President of the United States*
Vermont Royster, *William R. Kenen, Jr., Professor of Journalism and Public Affairs, University of North Carolina*
Milton Russell, *Senior Staff Economist, Council of Economic Advisers*
Jill Schuker, *Executive Director, New England Congressional Caucus*
Elvis Stahr, *President, National Audubon Society*
Stewart Udall, *Overview, Inc.*
Lloyd Unsell, *Independent Petroleum Association of America*
William Van Ness, *Committee on Interior and Insular Affairs*
Frank Zarb, *Administrator, Federal Energy Administration*